MEN AND IDEAS IN ENGINEERING

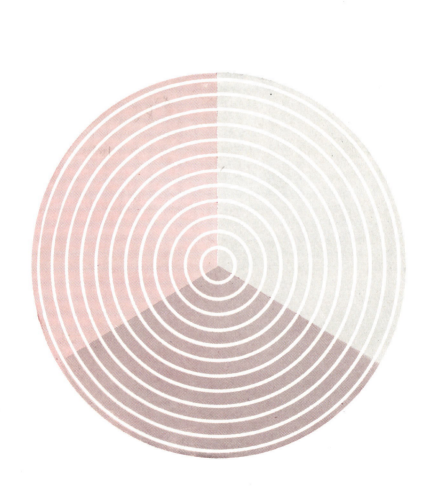

Men and Ideas in Engineering
Twelve Histories from Illinois

30€6€2

R. A. Kingery / R. D. Berg / E. H. Schillinger

PUBLISHED FOR THE COLLEGE OF ENGINEERING, UNIVERSITY OF ILLINOIS
BY THE UNIVERSITY OF ILLINOIS PRESS, URBANA · CHICAGO · LONDON, 1967

ACKNOWLEDGMENTS

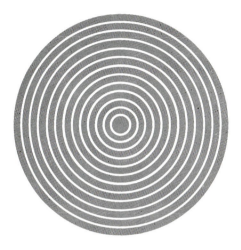

Many people helped in many ways in the creation of this book. While it is impossible to name them all, the reviewers who spent the most time and energy included: Dean W. L. Everitt, Ross Martin, Jack Desmond, Al Tillman, Bob Bohl, Tom Cooper, Paul Bryant, Dorothy Everitt, Stuart Umpleby, Dave Penniman, Barbara Bryant, Al Halpern, Ann Riggins, Grace Swanson, Lillian Heldreth, Catherine Cartland, Art Wildhagen, Mac Van Valkenburg, J. O. Smith, and Dave Salyers.

We owe thanks to the publishers of *Surgery, Gynecology, and Obstetrics,* and the Association for Computing Machinery, publishers of *Computing Reviews,* for their permission to use the material quoted in the chapters on ultrasound and computers. The cooperation of Sidney L. Pressey and the Department of Photography of The Ohio State University in providing photographs of early teaching machines, and the help of W. P. Trower in supplying bubble chamber pictures are gratefully acknowledged.

We owe special gratitude to Kay Jordan and Mary Ellen Irvin for typing and retyping the many versions of the manuscript; to Wayne Crouch for his extensive help with Chapter 2; to Ursula Weise for editing the manuscript; and to Binnie Williams for her advice and suggestions on matters of style.

We are grateful to these and the many other people who read, criticized, and improved the manuscript, and who encouraged, harassed, and forgave us.

CONTENTS

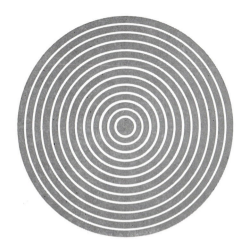

INTRODUCTION

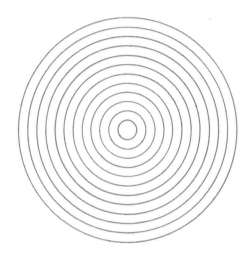

Engineering may be defined in many ways, none of them altogether satisfactory. One of the reasons for this is that the field changes so rapidly. This book, while not a history, provides examples of such changes at the University of Illinois. Generally, these examples reflect similar changes during the same period across the entire field of engineering research and education.

One hundred years ago at Illinois, as in most colleges of engineering, there was little or no tradition for conducting research. Discovering new knowledge was considered inappropriate for institutions dedicated to disseminating time-honored facts. By the first of the century University engineers began to recognize the importance of research, and programs of testing associated with boilers, locomotives, timber, and coal were initiated. The College of Engineering, using an unorthodox scheme of organization, included the Physics Department—an arrangement which would add breadth to the College's research.

Interest in research broadened during the twenties and thirties as programs with heavy emphasis on applications gave way to more creative research dedicated to the development of new techniques and devices. World War II added a new dimension to research as engineers and scientists overstepped the traditional boundaries of their professions to work together on government projects. The atomic bomb was the product of one of these groups, composed of specialists from a number of fields. After the war, the interdisciplinary team approach was continued in peacetime research at the universities, especially at Illinois.

By the end of the Korean War, financial support from Washington had radically changed the nature of research and the researcher. The research professor, so often caricatured as an idealist living in an "ivory tower," took on projects involving vast sums of money, and with them all the anguish associated with such heavy responsibilities.

The research dollars from Washington brought affluence to engineering education. Someone said, "The greatest discovery of American science after the war was the U.S. Treasury." Much of the money was earmarked for "pure" or basic research. It had become clear that a research program undertaken to learn what could be learned, with no narrowly defined goal in view, could yield unexpected results of the greatest significance to society.

Such programs, often requiring the researcher to seek not only answers to questions but also the questions themselves, put him in double jeopardy: the problem he set out to solve might not ultimately be worth the effort, and the solution he found might not be a good one. Success and failure were no longer clearly distinguishable; research endeavors had become so complex that often an engineering accomplishment could not be judged by any criterion other than the pragmatic. Only when it left the realm of engineering and was adopted for use by society could it be called successful.

The changes in the nature of engineering research in the College over the century were paralleled by changes in educational programs. When engineering research was "applied," so was engineering education; when research assumed a more basic character, the change was likewise felt in the classroom; and with the modern trend toward interdisciplinary research, there has been a trend toward the education of engineers to work in fields that cross the boundaries of technical areas established by tradition and past practice.

These stories, with their differences in methods and results, illustrate this evolution at Illinois during its first century. Perhaps the best definition of engineering is provided by the stories themselves.

THE BUILDING OF A THEORY

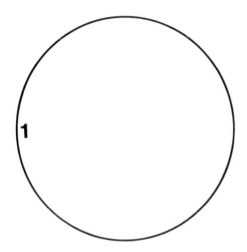

On July 28, 1957, Mexico's worst earthquake in 50 years devastated Mexico City. A dozen buildings collapsed and many more were so greatly damaged that they would have to be demolished. In nearly every large building there were shattered windows and broken plaster; sprung elevator shafts and broken plumbing were commonplace. Sidewalks were tilted as much as 45 degrees, and buildings that had been standing side by side were leaning apart at odd angles. The city was shattered.

Amid the rubble the city's tallest building, the 43-story Latino-Americana Tower, stood unharmed. Not a window or a partition in the giant building was cracked. The building's survival was not an accident. The story of its dramatic success had begun 80 years earlier with the arrival of a twenty-year-old engineering student on the campus of the Illinois Industrial University.

Arthur Newell Talbot came to the campus in 1877 on a horse-drawn streetcar, the only public transportation connecting the University and the neighboring towns of Champaign and Urbana. This tiny, isolated outpost, consisting of a handful of mismatched buildings in the middle of the prairie, would eventually become the University of Illinois. Except for a four-year period, Talbot would spend the rest of his life here.

After graduating in 1881, he followed a boyhood interest in railroading and went to Colorado to survey for a narrow-gauge line through the mountains. In a letter to a friend in Urbana, he described the job and some of his co-workers: "The workmen of our party are mountain roughs; gamblers and jailbirds some of them are. When the engineer of the party took us up to the bar on our arrival,

The site of the engineering campus as seen by Talbot when he arrived in 1877

and I called for lemonade, there was an audible smile which went over the boss' face as well as the rest of the crowd, ten in all, who all took their whiskey." Such attitudes set the tone for Talbot's relationships with people all his life.

In 1885 Talbot, now twenty-eight years old, came back to his alma mater as an assistant professor of engineering and mathematics. These were depression years and the 28 faculty members earned average salaries of $2,000 (not including Regent Peabody, who made $4,000). Salaries had been declining along with student enrollments. It was hardly an auspicious start for a career.

Talbot's first assignment was in the Civil Engineering Department. There he began teaching courses in the new subject of engineering mechanics, and in 1890 the University administration recognized its popularity and importance by organizing the Theoretical and Applied Mechanics Department. Talbot was placed in charge of this department, a position he would occupy during the rest of his career at the University. His jaw-breaking title was "Professor of Municipal and Sanitary Engineering in Charge of Theoretical and Applied Mechanics."

The new department head prided himself on his ability to learn the names and faces of all his students in a single class meeting; his lectures, however, were impersonal and always seemed to be addressed to the back wall of the room. In his course TAM 6, Engineering Materials, he would enter the classroom and lecture through the period without ever looking at the class. Many of the students called this course "Sleep 6" and him "Stoneface."

Talbot once decided to illustrate his lectures with slides. The lights were turned off during the first lecture. When they were switched on again, the room was empty except for the projectionist and Talbot.

The "Stoneface" label might have applied to his family life as well—he was a 24-hours-a-day engineer who spent his own time reading technical journals, even during meals. His vacations were often spent reading and writing technical articles with the help of a secretary who sometimes accompanied him and his family on these holidays.

Talbot's accomplishments in research brought him recognition early in his career. His formulas for relating the rates of rainfall runoff to the sizes of waterways became standards for engineering practice. He developed the "Talbot Spiral" or "railroad transition spiral," a flexible method of laying out gradual, jolt-free railroad curves. At his urging, facilities for hydraulic studies and the testing of construction materials were established at the University. He pioneered in sewage treatment with septic tanks, testing of roadway materials, the design and use of reinforced concrete structures, and research on stresses in railroad rails.

In spite of the importance of these accomplishments, Talbot could never quite understand the fame he achieved. He once said that he thought the many awards and honors

Professor Arthur N. Talbot in 1886

he received could have been "accidents," many of the later ones coming because "once you get one, you get others." He felt that he lived in a time of opportunity when little had been done, and that his accomplishments were commonplace. "It has been surprise after surprise to find that my own work has been widely accepted, generally commended, and has received such continuing recognition."

Talbot did achieve an international reputation, but apparently neither he nor any of his contemporaries realized that his greatest claim to fame was the number of other outstanding engineers he attracted to his profession and the tradition of excellence he established at Illinois.

The first of the men who came to work with him was a dark-haired, gaunt-faced engineer named Wilbur Wilson. Wilson was thirty-two when he received a one-year appointment as an assistant professor in 1913. During that year, however, the Western Society of Engineers awarded him the Chanute Medal for the best paper of the year presented before the Society, and he was invited to stay at Illinois as a permanent staff member. Although he was popular with his colleagues and students, Wilson did share Talbot's Calvinistic attitude toward life: their co-workers were afraid to smoke, chew, or swear near either of them.

Early in his career Wilson became a proponent of a newly developed structure, the rigid-frame bridge. Cheaper to construct and maintain, as well as stronger than older style bridges, the rigid-frame bridge was a simple structure with top and sides of one solid piece of reinforced concrete. The design was so novel that it took many years to gain acceptance, but eventually it became the most popular kind of small bridge.

Wilson was as interested in the deterioration of bridges and other structures as he was in their design. His work

A rigid-frame bridge over the Pennsylvania turnpike

with metal fatigue enabled engineers to determine the most likely locations of fatigue cracks, so that the flaws could be detected before they endangered the life of the structure.

One winter day, while testing a bridge to learn how temperature was affecting it, Wilson worked so long in the cold that he froze part of one hand. Because of this experience and because he disliked waiting for years to observe fatigue developing naturally in buildings and bridges, he

Wilbur Wilson conducts a test of a riveted joint. The development of testing machines by Wilson and others enabled engineers to study structural materials and fasteners more rapidly and precisely.

joined Herbert F. Moore, famed for his work with metal fatigue, in designing and building testing machines that would give the same results in the laboratory in much shorter periods of time. Many of these testing machines were used for decades on the Illinois campus, and similar machines were used in other laboratories around the world.

In the last years before he retired in 1949, Wilbur Wilson made his greatest contribution to engineering. In designing, constructing, and testing structural members, he had become interested in how they were fastened together. Joints were made primarily by two means, welding and riveting, and Wilson had done a great deal of research on both. Rivets were expensive to install and difficult to replace when they failed. Wilson was particularly concerned because in many structures, particularly bridges, rivets were failing at an alarming rate. If bolts were strong enough, he felt, many of these problems would be solved. His research indicated that joints fastened with high-strength bolts could be stronger than riveted joints.

Many engineers thought Wilson was crazy: "If rivets, which fill the holes completely, can work loose, how can you think that bolts won't?" But rivet and bolt manufacturers had more faith in Wilson, and they performed tests that agreed with his. As it became clear that bolts were not only stronger, but also easier and cheaper to replace than rivets, engineers began to realize the fasteners' potential. Wilson was instrumental in the formation of the Research Council on Riveted and Bolted Structural Joints, and through that organization carried on further research. Eventually such structures as the Pan American Building in New York City, which used over four million high-strength bolts, and the Verrazano Narrows Bridge, with three million, would testify to the value of Wilson's idea.

The next man after Wilson to join the structural engineering team was Harald M. Westergaard. "The Great Dane," as he was called, had been studying in Germany when World War I started. He found it necessary as a foreign national to leave quickly. "Go to Illinois and study under Talbot," a friend advised, and Westergaard followed the advice. He was one of the first students to qualify for a Ph.D. in theoretical and applied mechanics at Illinois, and in 1916 he became a member of the staff.

Westergaard was an unusual man. He was a scholar with a wide range of interests, an ability to speak and read a number of languages, and an exceptional talent for theoretical and mathematical problems. Unlike Wilson, he disliked working with his hands. He had one known affectation: he carried a cane because "one should have an eccentricity to be remembered by." He was as likely to be remembered for his absent-mindedness. Sometimes he drove his car to work, forgot it, and walked home.

Westergaard fit the picture of an aloof, erudite professor, but his reputation as a "loner" was not fully deserved. Slightly deaf, he was often preoccupied with his thoughts. "If Doc ever snubbed you," one associate said, "it was for one of three reasons: he didn't hear you, he was thinking about something else, or you were such a hopeless fool he couldn't tolerate you."

He was not an easy man to meet. Because he disliked coming to work early, he sandwiched his regular office hours into the ten-minute periods between his morning classes. A little sign on his office door read: "Office Hours—10:50 to 11:00 A.M., Monday, Wednesday, and Friday."

But the Great Dane was an outstanding speaker and writer. To many of his students his insistence on precision and style seemed to border on fanaticism. He was seldom appreciated by undergraduates, but he was a remarkable graduate instructor. His exams sometimes contained trick questions that his students either saw through and answered immediately or never managed to answer at all.

Westergaard's meticulousness and originality were unmixed virtues for research. He was an expert in structural mechanics, the analysis of pavement slabs, and the effect of earthquakes on structures. His studies of Japanese earthquakes with Mikishi Abe, a Ph.D. student of Professor Talbot, had an important influence on Japanese building design.

Westergaard became the special analyst for the Stevenson Creek experimental arch dam in California, and was later hired as chief mathematician on the specialized design problems of Hoover (Boulder) Dam. Part of his work was to determine the degree of earthquake resistance necessary for the intake towers in Lake Mead. Another part involved calculating the stresses that could be imposed on the ground by the world's largest man-made lake.

While Westergaard was establishing his reputation, another man joined this brilliant circle of structural engineers.

Hardy Cross, an engineer-philosopher whose specialty was structural analysis and design, came to Illinois in 1921. The man who would become known as the greatest teacher of structural engineering of all time looked to his students like a bad-tempered, sarcastic perfectionist. Cross, like Westergaard, suffered from deafness, and he used this handicap to his own advantage both in and out of the classroom. Students found it difficult to improvise answers at the tops of their voices, and soon learned either to be explicit or to admit that they couldn't answer his questions.

In the classroom Cross lectured without notes, but his performance was always calculated to create the atmosphere he wanted. Occasionally he would stomp out of the classroom early because no one had attempted a certain problem, then later ask someone who had observed the exit, "How do you think they took it?" If everything had gone well in a class, Cross would walk to the door at the end of the period, smile at the students, and then rush out of the room. After observing one of these performances, Wilson remarked, "It's just like the Cheshire Cat's smile in *Alice in Wonderland*—it's still hanging there after he's gone!"

Sometimes he chose to play an intellectual devil's advocate. Once a student named Alford told Cross that he thought one of the problem solutions in their text was wrong. Cross paced back and forth, staring hard at the student, and pointing at him fiercely. "Can you, a graduate student, actually have the temerity to accuse the internationally known engineer who wrote this book of MAKING A MISTAKE? Can you really believe that the publishers would allow such an alleged error to be printed? Can you show us the error?"

Alford seemed unable to answer.

Still pacing, Cross said, "Can anyone help Mr. Alford? Do any of you see a mistake in problem four?"

The class was silent.

"Well, Mr. Alford," Cross said sternly, "would you care to retract your accusation?"

"It's just that I can't . . ."

"Speak up!" Cross thundered.

"I still believe it's wrong!" Alford shouted, his face red with embarrassment.

"Then kindly come to the board and prove it to us," Cross taunted. "We shall be pleased to see the proof of your unfounded allegation."

Alford labored at the board without success for the rest of the period.

Cross began his next lecture by saying, "In our last meeting Mr. Alford raised a serious and unfounded charge against the author of our text." Staring at Alford, he said, "Have you reconsidered your accusation?"

"No, sir," Alford replied. "I still believe he is wrong."

"To the board, then. We still await your proof."

Alford's labors were again unsuccessful.

The third time the class met, Cross said, "Mr. Alford, are you ready to withdraw your ill-considered accusation about problem four?"

Moments later Alford was at the board. Within a few minutes he managed to show that the solution to the problem in the book was incorrect, and he returned to his seat. Cross's pleasure was evident from his expression. "You must always have the courage of your convictions," he said. "Mr. Alford does; apparently the rest of you do not, or you are not yet sufficiently well educated to realize that authority—the authority of a reputation or the authority of a printed page—means very little. All of you should hope to someday develop as much insight and persistence as Mr. Alford."

Cross believed that the classroom was the place to develop the student's personal ingenuity and self-confidence. "The University is a place to get into as much intellectual trouble as possible, a place to make mistakes, many mistakes, and to rectify them."

Dean Milo Ketchum resented Cross's reputation as a great teacher. During his term as dean he had prevented Cross from getting salary increases, and had suggested a number of times that Cross might be better off working elsewhere. One of the charges Ketchum leveled against Cross was that he failed to publish enough papers, although Cross's publications between 1925 and the early thirties were among the most important and far-reaching of any written in the College during that period.

Finally, in answer to Ketchum's threats, Cross published a ten-page paper in the *Proceedings of the American Society of Civil Engineers* that was a classic. The paper, entitled "Analysis of Continuous Frames by Distributing Fixed-End Moments," set forth a new method of analyzing building frames. Cross won the Norman Medal of the ASCE for it, and the technique became known the world over as the "Hardy Cross method" or the "moment-distribution method."

Cross later quipped that there were "no further discussions with the Dean on the subject of my being a Cross the College wouldn't bear."

Thus by the early 1920's structural engineering had become an important part of the University of Illinois. The

An important addition to the new Materials Testing Laboratory was this 3,000,000-pound compression and tension testing machine, installed in 1930. Wilson, delighted, watched the installation from beginning to end.

first-string team consisted of Talbot, founder of the tradition; Wilson, the experimentalist; Westergaard, the theoretician; and Cross, the philosopher. All of them drew other outstanding men to Illinois.

In 1930 the man who was to inherit the expertise accumulated over the years at Illinois came to the University to do graduate work in structural engineering. Nathan M. Newmark was a brilliant student who had earned a bachelor's degree from Rutgers University before he was twenty years old. Like many others, he came to study under the giants of the field at Illinois.

In Newmark's first encounter with the engineer-philosopher Hardy Cross, Cross asked where each student had studied. When Newmark answered, "Rutgers," Cross looked down his nose and answered, "You've got a lot of things to unlearn."

But in time Newmark and Cross developed a mutual admiration and a broad spectrum of interests. Their relationship was based on the interplay and exchange of ideas—not only in engineering, but in every conceivable subject. They discussed with equal relish politics, philosophy, art, or anything else that interested them. As Newmark put it, his part in these discussions "must have been audible for blocks" because Cross was so deaf.

Newmark's initial appointment was as a research assistant working under Professor Wilson. In 1934 he received the third Ph.D. ever awarded by the Civil Engineering Department. Because of his outstanding work, Wilson recommended that a permanent position be created for him on the civil engineering staff. In a letter of recommendation for this appointment Cross said, "He is, I think, the ablest man we have ever had in graduate work. He has a great power for originating methods and viewpoints." In another letter Westergaard said, "I believe that his appointment will be a contribution to the solution of the difficult problems, a source of future distinction for the University. His intellectual capacity is rare, his personality attractive. He is among the few who can be rated as truly brilliant."

The Dean and the head of the Department felt that Newmark's great potentialities could best be developed by allowing him to work on whatever interested him most. The first project he undertook was an extended, detailed study of stresses in building foundations.

The Materials Testing Laboratory, center for the University's structural research, was renamed the Arthur Newell Talbot Laboratory in 1938, 12 years after Talbot's retirement.

The team had begun to break up before Newmark joined it. Talbot, endowed with an international reputation, had retired in 1926. His pioneering work had touched on nearly every aspect of civil, hydraulic, structural, sanitary, and railway engineering, and his name was solidly linked with the diverse uses of concrete as an engineering material.

The second man to leave the team, Hardy Cross, resigned to take the position of Chairman of Civil Engineering at Yale in 1936. The following year Harald Westergaard resigned to become the Dean of the Harvard Graduate School of Engineering.

With Wilson's retirement in 1949 all four of the great engineers were gone from Illinois. They had been rewarded handsomely by the profession they had served. Between them they had accumulated ten honorary degrees, fifteen medals, four plaques, and a certificate of appreciation for determining the causes of ship plate fracture during World War II. Talbot had been especially honored by Illinois: the Materials Testing Laboratory had been renamed the Arthur Newell Talbot Laboratory. The engineers' monuments were everywhere: in buildings, railroads, highways, dams, culverts, and bridges. They left a tradition of excellence for the structural engineers who would follow them at Illinois—and their protégé, Nathan Newmark.

Newmark by now had had fifteen years to develop his own ideas. Deeply influenced by his predecessors, he was left to carry on the work the others had started.

In 1950 Newmark was given an opportunity to put into practice the knowledge that had accumulated during the last 70 years. The project would demand knowledge of all the aspects of structural engineering which had been the strongest interests of Newmark and his teachers: reinforced concrete, foundations, steel frame connections, and factors related to earthquake resistance. He was invited to serve as a consultant on the design of the Latino-Americana Tower in Mexico City.

It was a complex problem. The tower would be built in the heart of an area plagued by earthquakes, on the poorest subsoil imaginable for a tall building. Two of Newmark's former students, Leonardo Zeevaert and Emilio Rosenblueth, worked with him on the project. The steel for a 28-story building had been purchased and was on the site when Newmark arrived to discuss the project with the young Mexican engineers. They concluded that the building would be too weak for the earth motions it might be forced to endure.

Newmark suggested that with a better design the building could go as high as 43 stories. The redesigning began. The ground itself created problems: to a depth of 100 feet or more there was watery clay; below this were layers of fine sand, gravel, and more clay. Zeevaert and Newmark designed the Tower to stand on 361 one-hundred-foot concrete pilings that were driven down to the level of the sand, 117 feet below street level. The foundation was planned to behave as a floating box, sitting on these roots in such a way that the load of the building was carried by the piles to the thin, hard stratum of sand. The building was to be as light and flexible as possible. The tops and bottoms of all windows were anchored with single bolts, and small spaces were left between the tops of partitions and the ceilings. The building was designed to withstand earthquake tremors three times stronger than any previously recorded in Mexico City.

As completed, the Tower stood 43 stories high, with a 138-foot television antenna towering more than 600

The 43-story Latino-Americana Tower in Mexico City provided a critical test for the structural engineering theories developed at Illinois over a 70-year period.

feet above the city. Instruments were mounted at various elevations to record motions of the floor due to winds or earthquakes. Newmark's part of the work was concluded in 1954, and the structure became another part of his past.

After the earthquake of 1957, engineers went into the Tower and examined the recording instruments. The top of the building, they learned, had whipped back and forth approximately a foot. Cushioned by its special foundation, the gigantic structure had undergone almost exactly the forces it had been designed to withstand.

Many sightseers, walking or driving through Mexico City after the earthquake, were amazed to see the city's tallest building standing undamaged. Four of the men whose work had made the Tower possible would not have been surprised at all—but none of them were ever to see it.

THE MAN HISTORY FORGOT

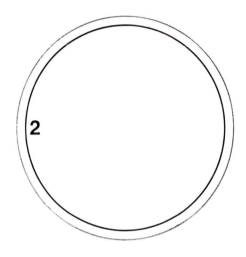

2

The Physics Building auditorium buzzed with the talk and noise of people entering and finding seats. It was a warm day in June, 1922, and the room temperature was rising rapidly because of the large crowd. Latecomers were still arriving when a small man, his high, starched collar shining brightly above his dark, double-breasted suit, strode onto the platform.

He was introduced as Joseph Tykocinski-Tykociner, a research professor in electrical engineering. The title of his lecture was long and technical, but most of the audience paid rapt attention to every word he said. They knew his discussion would introduce a device which would do something they had never seen.

The slightly built man told them how he had conceived the idea for his invention, and then he threw a switch on a tall black machine on the table in front of him. After the projector whirred for a few moments, a figure appeared on the screen at the front of the auditorium. A woman in a long, white dress held a bell: her lips moved, and the audience was astonished to hear her say, "I will ring."

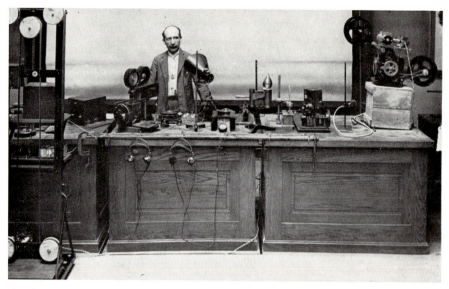

Joseph T. Tykociner used this conglomeration of equipment to give the world's first public demonstration of sound-on-film movies on June 9, 1922, at the University of Illinois.

Over the noise of the projector the audience clearly heard the bell. The woman (who was Mrs. Tykociner) then asked, "Did you hear the bell ring?"

It was the first sound-on-film movie ever publicly shown.

The film was short, but the demonstration was a double feature. Tykociner showed another piece of film that featured Ellery Paine, the head of the Electrical Engineering Department, reciting Lincoln's Gettysburg Address. Paine had selected the speech because he could think of no words of his own to say to a camera. Both his speech and his nervousness came through clearly, and the audience enjoyed it thoroughly.

News of the invention spread rapidly. Tykociner recalls that "A few days after the demonstration, Josef F. Wright, the head of public information for the University, brought me a whole armload of newspaper clippings. There were something like seven hundred."

The story made the *New York World* on Sunday, July 30, 1922. The headlines predicted, "Talking, Laughing, Singing Screen to Rival the Silent Drama Films." There were two long articles, one written by Tykociner and another by a *World* reporter. The latter made an interesting prediction: "Instead of registering silent contempt toward a certain personage the heroine will bawl, 'You villain!', her voice

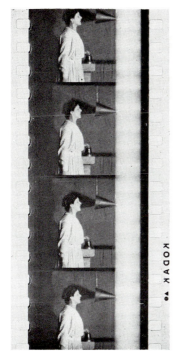

Mrs. Tykociner and Ellery Paine, head of the Electrical Engineering Department, starred in the first public demonstration of Tykociner's invention.

audible all over the theatre and projected simultaneously with the action on the screen."

Tykociner was quoted as saying, "The voices in an opera, the music, the orchestra, the dialogue can be recorded and reproduced. Many noted plays, comedies and farces that are not adapted to the screen because of the wit and humor of the dialogue, the personality of the actors, may now be revived and find new favor. I have great hopes that it will cause a revival of the masterpieces of dramatic art."

Near the end of his article the *World* writer said, "The inventor has given the University of Illinois an option on the promotion of the camera and he hopes that the University will find some way to exploit it commercially. But as science is the darling of the University, it may be difficult for the University to take up the commercial end."

He was right. As the reporter knew, universities had traditionally shown little interest in inventions and patents. In the 1800's and early 1900's this attitude was related to the idea that discovering new knowledge was not the proper business of a university. By Tykociner's day this philosophy had been discarded, but professors were ordinarily not encouraged to patent inventions unless they wished to do so on their own, with their own funds.

The demonstration was given less than ten months after Tykociner was hired as a research professor of electrical engineering at Illinois. But he had conceived the idea of photographically recording sound on the same strip of film with a motion picture a quarter of a century before. The idea had grown out of an even earlier desire to make a better phonograph. In his newspaper article Tykociner described the origin of the concept:

When at school about thirty years ago, I was very much interested in phonographs and in telephone receivers and was struck with the marvelous working of the telephone compared with the indistinct reproduction of speech by phonographs. It occurred to me that the way of making a perfect phonograph would be to discard the mechanical method of recording sound and to do it somehow electrically. Since then my thoughts were preoccupied searching for such a method.

Tykociner was born in Vloclawek, Poland, in 1877. After secondary school he wanted to study electrical engineering, but his family considered his plans unwise. Besides the high cost of tuition, engineering schools required entering students to have some practical experience. Tykociner was not interested in a factory apprenticeship; he knew that the long hours of work would allow little time for studying and experimenting, and was determined to find a job that would allow him to do both.

In March of 1896 he sailed for America. He spent the passage in his crowded quarters in the hold thinking of ways to make a better phonograph. By the end of the trip he had an answer. The membrane of a telephone receiver might be connected to a device that would control a light source, and the variations of the light intensity could be photographed, thus recording the original sound. To reproduce the sound a ray of light passing through the sound track of the film could be converted into a fluctuating electric current. The current could then be amplified to drive a telephone receiver, and reproduce the original sound. The outstanding feature of the idea was that the record would be made photographically instead of mechanically, so that there would be no losses from friction and inertia.

Tykociner wanted to develop this idea after he arrived in America, but he could not find living conditions that would allow him to work on the project. He found his first job in Newark, New Jersey, with the Electric Car Lighting Company, where he was assigned to help in the process of making special, lightweight batteries. He was fascinated with the work and persistently questioned fellow employees until he understood the whole manufacturing process. By this time he had mastered the intricacies of his own job, and the foreman was beginning to feel that his new employee might be productive after all. Then Tykociner asked for a different job.

"Is there something wrong with the job? Are the other workers hard to get along with?" the foreman asked.

"No," Tykociner replied, "but I understand everything now."

The foreman suggested that Tykociner either get back to work or get out. Tykociner sadly accepted the fact that this company was not interested in educating him and started hunting for a new job.

He moved from job to job, always trying to learn as much as possible about the work in which he was involved. Besides working, he enrolled for night school at New York's Cooper Union and managed to squeeze in some experiments on his idea for a better phonograph. Part of his work was done in the workshop of the college, and some in a makeshift laboratory on an unheated back porch.

Although the phonograph was still unfinished, a simple experience stimulated him to envision the instrument as a device that could make movies talk. He saw a sign in a small Broadway shop: "See the Latest Wonder, the Bioscope. Only 25 cents." He described the show in the *New York World* article:

I saw projected upon the screen athletic, military and simple dramatic scenes. It was the first time I saw moving pictures. In a dark room marching soldiers were seen on the wall, performing movements under command of officers. No sound was heard other than the clicking noise of the projecting machine.

I was impressed by the technical achievement, but the absence of sound made the show unnatural, and especially the mute dramatic scenes seemed to me unendurable. The necessity of sounds and especially speech in addition to the visual illusion was so manifest that I could not help associating the working of my new phonograph combined with the projection of moving pictures.

In his experiments that spring and summer, Tykociner developed two models of a sound recording camera. In the first he used sound to control the pressure of a gas jet in a lantern, and moved a photographic plate past the flickering flame. It is remarkable that this model worked at all. Most photographic negatives of the day were made on glass plates, and Tykociner had to develop intricate methods of dropping the plates past the slit. He was unaware that flexible film had recently become available. Nor was he able to get fluctuations in the flame that corresponded exactly to the very small fluctuations of sound waves.

In his second model, the light passed through the opening of a vibrating shutter controlled by the diaphragm of a telephone receiver. This model was severely hampered because the shutters could not be moved rapidly enough. But Tykociner had discovered and purchased some flexible film, which made it easier to photograph the light fluctuations.

To reproduce the sound, Tykociner knew that he needed a light-sensitive selenium cell, an item that was commercially produced, but was rare and expensive. He tried unsuccessfully to borrow one from physics laboratories of colleges and universities in New York. Then one day he read in the paper about the work of the celebrated inventor, Nicola Tesla. It was evident from the story that Tesla had several selenium cells in his laboratory.

Tykociner called nervously at Tesla's office one afternoon. All the way to the office he had tried to phrase an explanation of his work and an eloquent request to borrow the selenium cell. He was awed by the man, but determined to solicit his help.

Tesla greeted him warmly, but his obvious willingness to help the young inventor was not enough. A few days before Tykociner's visit a disastrous fire had destroyed Tesla's laboratory. He no longer had any equipment. Forced to try to build a selenium cell himself, Tykociner was unsuccessful.

By the fall of 1897 Tykociner, having satisfied the university requirement of practical experience, returned to Europe to begin formal training in electrical engineering. As a student he continued his experiments, but had neither the time nor the resources to accomplish a great deal.

After graduating in 1901 he took a position with the Marconi Wireless Telegraph Company in England and became engrossed with the problems and challenges of improving radio. He undertook his assignments with the same energy and concentration that had characterized his work to improve the phonograph.

After two years' work in England he continued radio research with the Telefunken Company in Berlin. In 1904, when the Russo-Japanese War started, he was offered a responsible position introducing wireless into Russia on a large scale. Caught up in the First World War and the Russian revolutions, it would be 14 years before Tykociner could resume his sound recording experiments. He experimented with methods for underwater signaling by means of small explosions, and one of his achievements was the installation of a radio link between Russia's naval fleets in the Black Sea and the Baltic Sea. To accomplish this, he used the ship with the highest mast he could find—the Czar's yacht. He was personally rewarded by the Czar for his work.

In 1918, in the midst of the Revolution, Tykociner was allowed to leave Russia to return to his native Poland, but he was forced to leave many of his personal effects—including many of the records of his work on the new phonograph and talking movies.

Now, in the country of his birth, he again set to work to record sound on film photographically. But it was a time of revolution and chaos in Poland too, so he decided to return to America.

He went to work for the Westinghouse Electric and Manufacturing Company in Pittsburgh, Pennsylvania, where he asked for the company's support to develop sound-on-film. Their answer was short: "It's not in our line. Let the movie people do it."

He decided to look for the freedom he wanted at a university. After he had written several schools, he received a letter from one he had not contacted. It was an invitation from Ellery Paine, head of the Electrical Engineering Department at the University of Illinois, to consider a position there.

Tykociner could not know that a University faculty member in electrical engineering named Trygve Jensen, whom he had never met, was to be one of the most important people in his life.

Early in the 1900's Jensen had performed valuable research work on the magnetic properties of iron. In 1916 he angered the University by going to work for Westinghouse and taking his patents with him. Professor Paine had done research in the Westinghouse Laboratories, and had many friends there. Embarrassed by the Jensen incident and hoping to send him as good a man as the one they had taken, they told Paine about Tykociner. This information had triggered the unexpected letter.

Concerned about further patent losses, the University passed a statute stating that any employee who used University resources to produce an invention should patent it and turn control of the patent over to the University for one dollar. The inventor was to share in the royalties. Tykociner's interests and this new University patent policy were to come into conflict a few years later.

In the correspondence that followed the initial letter, Tykociner was assured that ". . . our research men . . . may be permitted to initiate and carry on investigations in which they are particularly interested." He left for Urbana immediately.

Tykociner and Paine first came face-to-face in the fall of 1921. Paine suggested some possible areas of research, but Tykociner was not interested. His enthusiasm returned when Paine asked him what he had in mind.

"I want to record sound on film."

Paine was surprised. "You can't photograph sound."

"Certainly not," Tykociner said. "But it is possible to photograph a light modulated by sound."

Most of the Department's research was in power engineering, so Tykociner's idea was in an area unfamiliar to Paine. "Can you prove it will work?" he asked.

The question annoyed Tykociner. "Prove it? That's why you do research."

Paine was still cautious. "If you can show a committee of engineering faculty that your idea of photographing sound has merit, we will support your research."

The demonstration, which was of urgent importance to Tykociner, took three weeks to prepare. After explaining his ideas about converting sound into variations of light on film to the faculty committee, Tykociner pushed a button and a small bar of light appeared on a screen. As he spoke into a telephone transmitter the intensity of the light changed noticeably and bands formed across the slit, approximately corresponding to the sound of his voice.

Tykociner explained that he needed to refine his equipment to produce a more accurate image of sound, photograph it, and find a way to convert the photographic record back to sound. Excited by the idea, the committee members offered the support which Tykociner had sought over two continents for 25 years.

In the Physics Building where he was given a laboratory, Tykociner soon met Jacob Kunz, the physicist who had invented the photoelectric cell. Tykociner immediately saw how this device could be used in place of the selenium cell.

His most difficult problem was solved, but the application

Tykociner holds a photoelectric cell, an important component of the sound-on-film projector.

of the photocell was not as easy as he had hoped. He lacked technical assistance and auxiliary equipment, and usually had to borrow the cameras and projectors he needed.

Tykociner borrowed vacuum tubes from the student-operated radio station and a motion picture projector from the College of Agriculture. The tubes had to be returned to the radio station each evening so that it could go on the air, and Agriculture would not allow Tykociner to remodel its projector. Film and electronic equipment were expensive, and the Department's research budget was small. He was forced to make a great deal of his own equipment and supervise the development of his film.

By March of 1922 he had made a short talking movie

with a sound track like that used on modern sound film. People who saw the preliminary demonstration were interested, but few were enthusiastic. Tykociner was becoming discouraged: his project needed more money, and few of his fellow faculty members were excited about his work.

Early that spring he received a telephone call which revived his battered outlook: "This is the President's secretary speaking. The Board of Trustees and the President would like a demonstration of your invention. When can you arrange a showing?"

"Why—in two weeks," he replied.

Two weeks later the President and Trustees, impressed with the demonstration, suggested that additional support might be available. Tykociner began to prepare for a public demonstration.

On May 4, 1922, W. L. Abbott, Chairman of the Board of Trustees, sent the report of the Tykociner invention to University President David Kinley with the following explanation:

> You will see from this report that patents which would apply to the fundamental processes would be for things done before Mr. Tykociner came to the University. Since he is willing, I think we should have him apply for the patents and make arrangements with him afterwards.

The University could hardly demand ownership of patents on ideas conceived and developed by Tykociner prior to his arrival at the University. The patents were his, and the University's interest in them would have to be decided by negotiation with Tykociner.

Tykociner exhibited his process publicly on June 9. The public was enthusiastic, but many of his engineering colleagues regarded the invention as a toy instead of a real scientific effort.

On July 28 J. M. White, Chairman of the Committee on Patents and Inventions, wrote to Eugene Davenport, Vice-President of the University:

> President Kinley has agreed to recommend an appropriation of $10,000 for the promotion of this work. It seems to me this appropriation should be contingent upon the University entering into a contract with Professor Tykociner for the assignment of these patents and the promotion of the invention. Professor Tykociner is fearful that the University will not promote this work rapidly enough so that he may derive the benefit which he feels he should receive from his invention.

Skepticism of the invention was growing. Everyone was developing theories to prove why the public would never accept talking movies—theories like "human beings were just not meant to handle two illusions at once."

To encourage the University to promote his work, Tykociner proposed two plans for sharing his patents with the University: the best way, he felt, would be for the University to set up a special department or corporation to administer further research and development. He would assign his patent rights in return for a guarantee that he could continue to develop his sound pictures, and organize a center for producing educational films. He wanted a minimum of $10,000 per year for himself.

As an alternate proposal, he would maintain control of the patents, and the University would receive five per cent of the total profits for every $10,000 that it invested; if the University did not provide enough help, he could accept outside support.

In a letter to the Dean of the College of Engineering on October 18, 1922, Tykociner said:

> If the technical and commercial development of my invention, as I have proposed it, cannot be undertaken by the University, I hope the College of Engineering will be in a position to obtain funds which will enable me to continue on a scale somewhat larger than at present. . . .

Early in November he called on President Kinley to state his case in person. He hoped to persuade Kinley to assist in the commercial development, or at least to get his assurance of sufficient funds to continue his research. Kinley told Tykociner that he considered such commercial agreements improper, and that he would not allow further scientific research on sound-on-film unless the University controlled the basic patents. Tykociner did not waver. If the University would not agree to his conditions he would not surrender the patents. Neither man budged.

Kinley spelled out the final verdict in a personal letter to Tykociner soon after the meeting:

> The University cannot with propriety promote research work by any member of its staff whose main interest and purpose in his research is the promotion of the commercial application in his own interest of whatever scientific principles he may discover.
>
> The University could acquiesce in and assist in research under the conditions described in paragraph 1 only if the worker were willing, in accordance with the rule of the Board

of Trustees, to assign to the University his rights in any patent which might properly be expected to issue as a result of his discoveries. I hope I made it clear to you this afternoon that in making this requirement the University will always endeavor to care for the interests of the individual, and will, I am sure, never take advantage of such assignment of possible patents to the detriment of any individual concerned.

We shall have to ask you, if you decide to continue working with us, to devote yourself to some other problems which shall not have the appearance of promoting the investigation whose commercial development is of so much personal interest to you.

The University officially dropped its support of the patent application and any claim to Tykociner's work. The professor stayed away from the University for several days, unable to go near the laboratory. It was the worst defeat of his career.

Halfheartedly, he visited the General Electric Company in Schenectady, New York. GE was not interested, and neither were the movie producers in New York (which was then the film-making capital). Defeated, Tykociner returned to Urbana. The words of George Eastman, undisputed leader of the film industry and a man noted for his ability to respond to the demands of the public, rang in his ears: "I wouldn't give a dime for all the possibilities of that invention. The public will never accept it."

The ridicule of Eastman and others who were actually involved in the movie-making industry did what the skepticism of his colleagues could not. After investing almost three decades pursuing a single idea, Tykociner gave up.

Despite Eastman's forecast, others were still working on methods of recording sound photographically. In March, 1923, Lee De Forest gave his first demonstration. The Western Electric Company licensed the manufacture of talking motion pictures in 1926, and Warner Brothers ventured into talkies.

Both Western Electric and Warner Brothers used separate, mechanically synchronized systems which have since been discarded, and Lee De Forest is credited with the invention of the sound track film method which is used today—the same system Tykociner had publicly demonstrated in June of 1922.

Tykociner continued to work at the University until his retirement in 1946, performing research in photoelectricity, detection of faults in high-voltage cables, piezoelectricity, and microwave transmission and reception. He developed a system by which scale models of large antennas could be made to exhibit the same characteristics as their larger, out-of-door counterparts, and such models are seen today in antenna labs around the world.

After retirement, Tykociner devoted all his time to expanding and writing about a new interdisciplinary science that he had developed over the past 30 years. "Zetetics" was designed to furnish guidelines that would allow the planning and management of research programs, encourage the combination of previously unrelated sciences, and examine the processses which lead to discoveries and inventions. But support for zetetics has been scarce.

"With sound-on-film," he says, "others carried out the idea and commercialized the process—and the University lost out. Perhaps outsiders will not step in this time and help popularize the idea—and zetetics will be lost for a long time or forgotten completely.

"The University has changed a great deal. Fifty years ago I had to give up one idea because it was 'too commercial.' Now I can't find support for zetetics because it is 'not commercial enough.'"

But Tykociner was not completely unrewarded for his more than 25 years of relentless effort to develop sound-on-film. He received $100 from the *New York World* for his article predicting the future of talking film. And all of his predictions came true.

A CAREER BUILT ON AIR

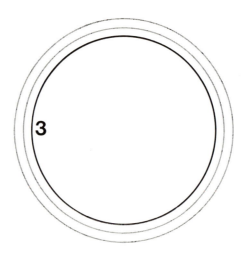

3

As the bell rang, the new assistant professor quickly gathered his papers and dismissed his class of would-be mechanical engineers. As usual, no one stayed behind to chat with the instructor. His aristocratic bearing awed the farm-bred students of this Midwestern university.

The teacher was Arthur Cutts Willard and the year was 1913. Tall, blond, smartly dressed in a pin-striped suit and cravat, the young professor looked more like a fashion model than an engineer—but his lectures, delivered with earnest, simple eloquence, showed that he was both a competent engineer and a dedicated teacher. Unknown even to himself, he was in training for an engineering project that would tie his name to one of the most outstanding engineering feats of the century.

Willard came to the University of Illinois from Washington, D.C., forfeiting a promising position as engineer in charge of sanitation and heating for army posts. Although an engineer by inclination and design, he somehow never managed to stray very far from the classroom. He had been principal of an exclusive prep school for boys in San Francisco seven years before, only to be shaken out of the city by the earthquake of 1906. In addition to his government job, he was teaching a number of courses in mechanical engineering at George Washington University when he decided to come to Illinois.

It was not the desire to teach again that had drawn the sophisticated Easterner to the small prairie communities of Champaign-Urbana, but a desire to learn more about the relatively unexplored fields of heating and ventilation. Although Roman engineers before the birth of Christ had devised astoundingly sophisticated methods of centralized home heating which utilized floor ducts and natural convection currents, their art was lost with the dissolution of the Empire. During the succeeding centuries, home heating did not progress beyond the fireplace. The Franklin stove, invented at the close of the eighteenth century, was a vast improvement over the open fireplace, but its performance was still undependable and its efficiency low. It was not until the early 1900's that central heating with wood and coal burning furnaces became commonplace in the United States.

The establishment of valid standards and the compilation of known information were necessary first steps toward further progress. The man who sought to make these steps was Louis A. Harding, who had come to the University at the same time as Willard to write a book pulling together all the miscellaneous data on heating and ventilating. At the time, knowledge about heating and ventilating consisted largely of untested theories and unrelated data gathered by the various companies that manufactured boilers, fans, and furnaces.

Harding had the practical knowledge and experience to compile and evaluate the material for such a book. He felt that as a coauthor Willard could help apply theoretical principles and draw conclusions from the mass of facts. He also enlisted the valuable analytical talents of thermodynamicist George A. Goodenough.

In 1916 the book, *Mechanical Equipment of Buildings*, was published by Wiley and Sons. For a technical handbook, it met with startling success. Within two years the first of the two-volume set could be found on every architect's and contractor's bookshelf, and it became the standard work on heating and ventilating. The success of the volumes, the first in particular, brought national recognition and advancement to the authors. Harding left the University the following year to accept a position as an engineering consultant. Willard, in the fourth year of his career with the University, was promoted to full professor.

In 1918 Willard appeared before the furnace manufacturers' trade association in Milwaukee, seeking their support for research on warm-air furnaces. He had realized the need for an accurate system of rating warm-air furnaces

A three-story house framework, built in the University's Mechanical Engineering Laboratory, made it possible to conduct heating and ventilating research under precise laboratory conditions.

while helping the government select furnaces for military buildings during the war. He felt that the natural laws and forces governing the flow of air over heated surfaces could be determined in the laboratory, and that the performance of furnaces could be stated in precise engineering terms. Impressed with the novelty of laboratory research on furnaces, the delegates pledged $5,000 to support the project for one year.

The selection of an assistant to supervise the research end of the investigation was Willard's first task. He chose Alonzo P. Kratz, a wiry little combustion engineer described as a "one-man whirlwind."

The combination of Kratz and Willard appeared to be a volatile one. Willard was reserved and formal—almost awesome in demeanor; Kratz, or "Kratzie" as the students called him, was a lively and outspoken Midwesterner known for his disheveled clothes and the pipe eternally clenched between his teeth. Despite their apparently great differences, they staked their careers and reputations on each other and their ability to work together.

The result was a very effective research team. Willard was an executive, an organizer. He emerged from his occasional forays into the laboratory as crisp and immaculate as when he entered. Kratz, on the other hand, reveled in the practical furnace work—the dirtier he became the less he cared. Willard was an idea man whose bursts of inspiration provided a continual supply of intellectual fuel for the investigation. Kratz made sure the ideas materialized. Time and again Willard, with a grandiose sweep of his hands, would soothe impatient industry representatives with his plans for new devices. It was up to Kratz to translate these promises into reality in the laboratory.

Defining the solution to the problem of rating warm-air furnaces proved to be far easier than providing it. They found that the only available instruments for measuring air velocity and temperature were unsatisfactory for precise laboratory conditions.

Proper equipment and instrumentation were an obsession with Willard. No makeshift orange-crate arrangements were acceptable in his investigations. He told his students, "Proper equipment goes with proper research," and many of them felt that his interest in equipment exceeded his interest in research. Carelessness with instruments was another failing which the director would not tolerate. One day

This two and one-half story research home was built to verify laboratory conclusions in an actual residence. It was equipped with gas analyzers, anemometers, thermometers, and miles of thermo-couple wires. Ground was broken for this home in 1922, and later other homes were built for warm air, steam, and hot water heating research.

he walked into the laboratory just as an undergraduate student who was calibrating a thermocouple dropped a thermometer.

"Young man, you have just broken an instrument that took thousands of years to develop," he chided. The student shrugged and replied that it only cost a few cents and could be replaced at any drug store. "Could you make a thermo-meter yourself for a few cents?" Willard snapped back.

It took seven years to develop the instruments they needed to measure the air temperature and velocity accu-rately. The work was tedious and time consuming, but the outcome was worth the delay. Foundrymen who had been skeptical of a scientific approach began to see the benefits of research. Once a uniform and dependable method of grading furnaces had been devised, the manufacturers won-dered whether research could answer other questions, such as the feasibility of thermostatic control and forced air (as opposed to gravity) furnaces. The success of the first phase of the investigation finally took the furnace industry out of the foundry and into the laboratory.

The furnace manufacturers were not the only ones who were pleased with Willard's work. In 1920 he was named head of the Mechanical Engineering Department.

Soon after the warm-air heating investigation began at Illinois, plans were completed half a continent away for one of the most ambitious engineering projects ever undertaken—a vehicular tunnel from New York to New Jersey under the Hudson River. Traffic, a problem that would not plague the rest of the world for years, was threatening to choke off the commercial arteries of Manhattan. Clifford Holland was chief engineer of the project.

The tunnel, consisting of two tubes each carrying two lanes of one-way traffic, would have a capacity of 1,900 vehicles per hour in each direction. It would span 9,250 feet, more than a mile of which would be under water. The longest existing vehicular tunnels were the Blackwall and Rotherhithe tunnels under the Thames in London. Constructed in the nineteenth century, these were only a third the length of the proposed New York–New Jersey tube and carried only a few dozen vehicles an hour. More significantly, they were short enough to be ventilated by natural air movement.

As Holland knew, ventilation would be a greater problem than excavation and construction. Past tunnels had been ventilated either by natural air currents or by simple mechanical systems involving a giant blower at one end of the tunnel and an exhaust fan at the other. For the New York–New Jersey tunnel, the latter method was not only impractical but dangerous. A blast sufficient to ventilate the entire length of the tube would have to enter at 280 mph and average 50 to 75 mph the entire length of the tunnel.

Gasoline motors and exhaust gases added serious complications that would have to be met by an effective ventilating system. Otherwise the tunnel would almost certainly become the world's largest and most expensive gas chamber. Because the ventilation question was such a vital one, Holland turned for help to three prominent research institutions—the U.S. Bureau of Mines, Yale University, and the University of Illinois.

Although the automobile had already become an American institution, almost nothing was known about the content of engine exhaust or its possible toxic effects. The Bureau of Mines ran tests on passenger cars and trucks of all sizes and makes, empty and loaded, with engines racing and idling, uphill and downhill, and on level roadways, to determine the content of exhaust gases. The investigation then moved to the Yale University laboratories for dilution studies. Test results indicated that carbon monoxide was the only harmful gas present in significant quantities.

Faculty members at Yale spent periods of one hour in a gas-tight chamber containing carbon monoxide-seeded air, and in a larger unventilated room where an automobile engine idled for an hour. The one-hour session was extremely liberal, since one could drive through the tunnel in half that time at only three miles per hour. The medical studies revealed that four parts of carbon monoxide per 10,000 parts of air was the maximum concentration permissible.

The practical phases of the investigation fell to the University of Illinois and Willard's ventilating experts, 900 miles from the tunnel site. The project was quite a prize for the University and for Willard. In Holland's report to the New York State Legislature, he referred to Willard as "one of the foremost authorities in this particular field of scientific research."

As Willard saw it, a successful tunnel ventilating system would have to meet many requirements: it would have to distribute fresh air uniformly throughout the tunnel, supply air unaffected by rain, snow, or dust in the outside atmosphere, provide easy control over the intake and removal of air, quickly dilute and remove exhaust gases, be free from high-velocity air currents, and remove smoke from accidental fires quickly.

Before the basic plan was reached, 21 ideas were studied and discarded. One of these went so far as to sidestep the exhaust problem altogether by transporting vehicles through the tunnel on a moving roadway. The final solution was to introduce and exhaust air through a number of openings along the roadway. The tunnel's curved lower portion beneath the roadbed would serve as an intake duct, and the corresponding area above the pavement would provide for exhaust. Huge blower fans eight feet in diameter would supply air along the bottom to adjustable openings in the walls. Exhaust fans would draw the spent air up through ports in the ceiling of the tunnel to stacks which would carry it to the surface. The Bureau of Mines and the Yale tests had indicated that 3,750,000 cubic feet of air per minute was necessary to keep the carbon monoxide ratio at a safe two parts in 10,000 parts of air.

On January 24, 1921, the Illinois group began constructing a model above-ground tube on Harvey Street, two blocks northeast of the engineering campus. Its dimensions were one-half those of one duct of the proposed New York–New Jersey tunnel. The test tunnel was fitted with a 300-horsepower fan and adjustable shutters to control the flow of air.

Tests proceeded routinely until one summer afternoon when the gauges unaccountably shot upwards, indicating that the air pressure in the tunnel had almost doubled. Willard dispatched his crew through the structure to find the cause of the mysterious change. After 15 minutes a research assistant returned to Willard and reported that he had found the trouble: a University couple was necking at the Springfield Avenue outlet. Drawn to the tube outlet by the cool blast issuing from it, they had unknowingly blocked the passage of atmospheric air, increasing the pressure inside the tunnel.

Goodenough was the project's mathematician. His rapid calculations gave Willard the intake equations for the Harvey Street tunnel and, by extrapolation, the equation for the New York–New Jersey tunnel. Willard and Holland felt that, by the same sort of procedure, the intake curves could be inverted to calculate the power needed to exhaust the air through the upper ducts. Kratz disagreed and performed laboratory tests to settle the matter. It took 17 attempts, but the stubborn experimentalist proved Willard wrong. He showed that it was necessary to take into account certain unpredictable currents which interfered with the removal of air through the ceiling.

The ventilation equations for the New York–New Jersey tunnel were completed in August. Goodenough, a perfectionist, was not completely satisfied. Months later he derived a universal equation from the one produced for the New York–New Jersey tunnel. It stated the intake-exhaust power relationships for every kind of underground construction project.

In the laboratory, a full-sized model of the air expansion chamber under the roadway was constructed with various shapes and sizes of openings. Studies were made to determine the proper angle of air flow—high enough not to raise road dust and low enough to allow the air to linger for some seconds at the passenger level before rising to the overhead exhaust system. These experiments also indicated the lowest pressure at which air could be forced through the slots.

Much to Willard's disappointment the final tests to verify

Illinois' conclusions were conducted not at Illinois but in an abandoned coal mine in Bruceton, Pennsylvania. A tunnel 135 feet below the surface of the ground was ventilated by the mine fan. Tests run by the Bureau of Mines with eight automobiles indicated that the University's specifications were more than adequate. Carbon monoxide content was well below the danger level. Ventilation with air moving from bottom to top, utilizing natural convection currents, proved to be more effective than downward ventilation, as Willard had expected. The equations held up beautifully.

The final specifications for the New York–New Jersey tunnel called for 84 giant fans, half of them blower and half exhaust. Operating with a total of 6,000 horsepower, the fans were to be housed in four 12-story structures located at the ends of the two tubes. The fans provided a complete change of air every 1.6 minutes—a surprising ratio since studies showed that air on average New York streets changed every 1.7 minutes.

The actual construction of the tunnel began in 1920. Subaqueous tunneling was not a new art: 22 railroad tunnels already lay buried around Manhattan Island. All had been constructed by the century-old shield process, in which the tunnel lining was constructed within a pressurized circular chamber or shield which advanced with the tunnel. This was the method which Holland chose for his tunnel, its chief advantage being that all construction could proceed beneath the river floor without interrupting the busy stream of traffic on the surface.

Once begun, work never stopped. The $48,000,000 project demanded 24 hours a day, seven days a week. During the seven years of excavation, millions of tons of mud and muck were removed and hauled in belt-driven cars to the surface. The tunnel pit was cold, deafeningly noisy, and damp. Mud covered everything. Khaki-clad "sand hogs" worked in compression chambers where the air pressure was almost double that of the atmosphere. The noise of the compression machinery drowned out all conversation and reduced communication to hand signals. Under these conditions the men tired rapidly, and despite elaborate safety precautions 14 died in tunnel accidents during the course of the excavation. Some were crushed by the massive hauling and digging machinery, and some died from lung diseases induced by the damp conditions of the tunnel. Both Holland and his successor, Milton H. Freeman, died while directing the project—"not from accident, but from the drain on their vital energy," according to one report.

All experimental evidence indicated that the ventilating problem had been solved. Only time, traffic, and the tunnel could offer final proof. Just before the official opening, a car was purposely set afire in the tunnel and the smoke successfully exhausted in less than two minutes. A still more primitive test involved a sniffing panel instructed to time the arrival and departure of a whiff of peppermint extract as it

The opening of the Holland Tunnel on November 13, 1927, saw more than 50,000 vehicles traverse the Hudson River in the new structure. (*Photo courtesy of Brown Brothers.*)

traveled from an uncapped bottle 1,000 feet down the tunnel.

On November 13, 1927, the new Holland Tunnel opened. During the first day between 50,000 and 60,000 curious motorists invaded the long-awaited structure. It was an unanticipated load, surpassing the proposed daily maximum by over 5,000 vehicles; yet the great lungs of the tunnel proved sufficient. Indicators showed that the carbon monoxide never rose above two parts in 10,000. Applauded the *New York Herald Tribune* the following day, "Although the tunnel harbored opening day more cars than it is ever likely to have again at one time, the air was fresh, dry, and cold, with less suggestion of gasoline fumes than one may detect on Fifth Avenue."

Perhaps the ventilating system passed its toughest test in the summer of 1949, when a 16-ton tanker truck carrying over two tons of inflammable chemicals exploded three-

The walls and ceiling were shattered by the blast when on May 13, 1949, a truck carrying 80 drums of inflammable carbon disulfide exploded inside the tunnel. Yet the ventilating system continued to function. (*Photo courtesy of Brown Brothers.*)

quarters of the way through the westbound tube. As an estimated temperature of 4000° melted more than a dozen trucks to a "mangled and heat-fused" mass of wreckage, and as noxious yellow smoke billowed amid the flames, the ventilating system continued to function. Although 60 persons suffered injuries, there were no fatalities. Within 56 hours the tunnel was reopened. It was a tragic yet brilliant monument to the engineers who had given it their collective best.

Seven years after the tunnel opened, Arthur Cutts Willard became the second engineer to be elected President of the

University of Illinois. Few periods in the University's history would be more trying or troubled than the ten years of his administration—years which would embrace both the Depression and the Second World War. In at least one respect, however, he had a head start on the office—he had always looked like a university president.

POWER BY PERSUASION

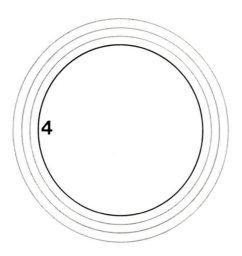

Ninety-four-year-old John Anderson stood before a group of his neighbors and local dignitaries on a farm near Ludlow, Illinois, and solemnly smashed a kerosene lamp against an electric light pole. The ceremony marked the passing of the kerosene lamp era in Champaign County; more significantly, it heralded the advent of electricity on the farms. It was 1938—almost 20 years after Illinois agricultural engineers began to promote rural electrification. It had been a long and frustrating battle because of the very people it was to help—the farmers.

The transition of the United States from an agricultural country to an industrial one had not been easy. While society was still largely agrarian, the farmer was often overcharged by the railroads that hauled his produce and the warehouses that stored it. He often could not get credit. He faced steadily falling prices. He went into debt.

Not until just before the First World War had the farmer's economic situation improved. Then in 1920, '21, and '22, he was hit by a severe depression that forced him to sell his crops at less than it had cost to produce them.

By the late 1920's, the farmer was nearly destitute. Never a strong consumer of manufactured goods, he now tried to reduce expenses by becoming self-sufficient. He tried to grow his own food, build his own fences and buildings, make his own clothes, and conduct his life so that if he should get any return for his labors, he could keep all of it. He was hardly inclined to believe that a small investment in modernization could bring him a better, happier life—particularly when the modernization involved the use of electricity, possibly the last thing he would have felt important to his life.

Rural electrification in Champaign County and in Illinois had begun long before the federal government and the bulk of the nation's farmers had realized the need for electricity on the farms. Much of the state's progress and the influence it had on the rest of the nation may be traced back to the early 1920's and to one man—a man with the foresight to recognize the plight of a major industry and a major segment of the population without power.

Emil Wilhelm Lehmann came to the University of Illinois in 1921 as head of the new Department of Farm Mechanics. He would occupy that position for 34 years. The youngest of ten children, Lehmann had grown up on a cotton farm in Mississippi where his German-born parents had settled. After earning bachelor's and master's degrees in electrical engineering from Mississippi and Texas A & M, Lehmann decided to combine his interests of farming and engineering. In 1914 he completed a degree in agricultural engineering at Iowa State University, and received a professional degree in agricultural engineering from the same institution in 1919.

As Lehmann saw it, the farm families' failure to recognize the importance of proper power and mechanization was the main barrier to farm modernization. He told the members of his department at Illinois in the first departmental meeting: "It isn't that we don't know how to help the farmers; it's just that they don't want to be helped. It's as if they're afraid of us, or maybe they're just afraid of changing."

The farmers' resistance to progress was nothing new to agricultural engineers. Problems which had plagued farmers for generations continued to plague those of the twentieth century. The annual race to harvest corn crops by hand before the weather and the market broke; mules and horses laid up for days with shoulders rubbed raw under loose harnesses; weeks of isolation following spring rains on dirt roads—these were the grim and timeless realities of rural life as it had been for centuries.

By 1920 a few daring farmers were beginning to experiment with motorized tractors, radical departures from the dependable plow horses which had served their agrarian masters since early times. But such innovators were in the minority. With the exception of gasoline engines, which were used sparingly about the farmsteads as energy sources for water pumps and belt-driven machinery, farm living had not changed appreciably for centuries. Limited production and small-scale farming made it impossible for individual farmers to amass enough capital to bring progress to their operations; on the other hand, there could be no production increases until agriculture moved into the twentieth century. Small wonder the U of I agricultural engineers adopted as their slogan, "The Profession with a Future." Agriculture had only one way to go—forward.

Lehmann was convinced that standards of living and work within the rural community could be and had to be improved. This was a novel concept to most farmers, who had accepted their sunup-to-sundown work day and the backbreaking drudgery of their labor when they chose their profession. More important than Lehmann's conviction were the tireless energy and dogged persistence he possessed and demanded from all who worked with him. Lehmann found that if he could not get what he wanted in any other way, he could talk most opponents into agreement. Lehmann's energy and tenacity may have caused some unhappiness in the Department, but they also produced results. One University official remarked that if he sent out a letter asking for suggestions concerning any problem, he could always count on at least one reply—Lehmann's.

Lehmann had first recognized the potential of electricity for farm labor at Texas A & M. His thesis topic there had been the use of electricity in agriculture. Measuring the electrical energy consumed by washing machines, ranges, refrigerators, and almost every other piece of equipment he could find in the community, Lehmann produced data which indicated that the farm household's potential electrical appetite surpassed that of a city family because of the necessity of refrigerating and preserving foods. He speculated that there was an untapped potential for electrical labor-saving devices around the farmstead, too.

With mobile demonstration units such as this, Lehmann tried to convince farmers of the usefulness of indoor plumbing.

Early in his career as head of the Agricultural Engineering Department at the University of Missouri, Lehmann became noted as a pioneer in rural home improvements. He organized traveling demonstrations of home improvements which he took around the countryside. The exhibition truck hauled an open two-story frame structure with kitchen plumbing on the first level and bathroom fixtures on the second. Groups of farm families would gather at the home of a neighbor to hear Lehmann expound on the convenience and value of indoor pumps, bathtubs, and toilets. For a rural population with few outside distractions, the demonstrations were festive outings for the entire family. But response to the lectures, though polite and interested, was disappointing. These were audiences that prided themselves on their frugality and practicality.

On one occasion, when Lehmann was having particular difficulty convincing the farmers that they could afford home improvements and that appliances were worth their cost, he caught sight of a pickup truck with a crate in the back of it. In the crate was a dog. "Mind telling me, sir, how much you paid for that hound dog?" Lehmann called to a man leaning against the truck.

"Thirty-eight dollars," the man called back, "plus two dollars for shipping."

"Don't you realize that for that amount of money you could have a pump right in your kitchen, so that your wife wouldn't have to go outside every time she wanted water?"

"That may be," the man replied, "but I bet that sink can't tree a coon."

Unlike engineers in other fields, whose research findings were directed to industry, the agricultural engineers dealt directly with their consumers—the farmers. Individuals were not likely to gamble their incomes on new ideas when the old ones had proved workable over a period of years. Thus the agricultural engineer was forced to do more than teach and do research—he also had to sell.

In 1920, less than 10 per cent of rural America was served by electricity. By comparison almost all of Holland's farms, 90 per cent of Germany's, and 50 per cent of Sweden's were electrified. Although population density on the European continent made electrification there easier and cheaper, the absence of electricity on American farms was especially deplorable to men like Lehmann because of the nation's generally high standard of living. For every farm family with electric power there were four with automobiles and two with telephones.

Lehmann wanted to show the farmers that adequate electrical equipment could save them money as well as provide conveniences and comfort. The power companies, too, needed to be convinced that there was a profitable market for their service in the corn-covered land as yet unbroken by transmission lines.

The utilities could profitably provide service to city dwellers at 35 customers per mile of line, but they balked at the idea of extending this service to the more sparsely populated rural areas. Even small towns had to rely on local power plants. There was almost no provision for the 230,000 Illinois farm homes. Individual generator units producing up to one kilowatt of electricity were available to those few farmers who could afford them. These were intended for lighting, the one innovation which appeared useful to most farmers. In the words of Professor Lehmann, lighting made it possible to "read the current events of the day, study various farm problems, and plan for the next year's work" after it was too dark to work outside. Concerning any other use of electric power, however, skeptical farmers asked, "Even if we could afford it, what would we use it for?" Lehmann reasoned that a lower rate for increased service would spur farmers on to find new uses for electric power, a proposition that could mean profit for the farmers—and for the utilities.

In 1923 his group at Illinois conducted an initial study on northern Illinois farmsteads served by power lines. The results of the investigation were disappointing. They emphasized rather than disproved the risk involved for power companies in rural neighborhoods. Of the 93 farm homes having electric service, all were lighted by electricity. However, only half the consumers used electric motors for limited power operations like pumping, grain grinding and elevating, and household operations. Most of their power was supplied by windmills; gasoline engines made up the difference.

The following year Lehmann, in cooperation with the local power companies, set up an experiment of his own—a three-year practical study of electricity in rural Tolono. Ten farms were wired to determine whether sufficient electricity would be used to make the installation profitable for both the farmers and the utility companies. More important, from Lehmann's point of view, was the opportunity to use these farms just as he had the plumbing exhibitions—as demonstrations that electricity and agriculture worked well together.

During the first year of the experiment, electrical equipment was provided free of charge by manufacturers to the families with an option to purchase after the first year. In addition to lights, all ten families were given refrigerators, vacuum cleaners, and cream separators. Utility motors, dishwashers, food mixers, ranges, grain elevators, and buttermakers were also made available. Although manufactured commercially, most of the household appliances were considered luxury items even in the urban areas.

During the study, the farm women often used their appliances to make cookies and cakes for the scores of curious farmers who dropped in to see the electrified farms. Professor Lehmann was a frequent visitor, and became a close personal friend of the cooperating farm families. Though he was serious and a bit formal in his relationships with the agricultural engineering faculty, Lehmann relaxed and enjoyed his Tolono friends. Once, after an evening meeting at the home of a cooperator, Lehmann led the group in a lively jig. One of the men recalled, "When I first saw him I thought, 'Here's a city fellow from the University going to

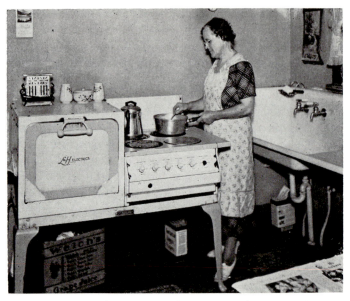

Such luxuries as the electric range and toaster were slow to find their way into farm kitchens.

tell me how to run my farm.' But after I got to know him, I knew he was just a farmer like me—only educated."

He became particularly fond of Mr. and Mrs. Harry Reifsteck. Mrs. Reifsteck, a young bride who had come to her husband's farm less than a year before, was used to the greater comforts and conveniences of city living. She felt that the heavy labor associated with farm household tasks deprived a woman of the intellectual and spiritual activities which made her life interesting. "It is possible for a farm wife to be a good housekeeper, but not a good homemaker. There is quite a difference in the meaning of these two words. I would much rather that people said I was a good homemaker than merely a good housekeeper." She found that electricity gave her time for both.

So enthusiastic was her acceptance of electrical living (she and her husband tried every piece of equipment available and eventually bought all but the electric ironer) that Lehmann decided to enlist her help in convincing other farm women of the advantages to be gained with electricity.

The small woman soon became a familiar sight on the rural roads in her blue Ford coupe. At Home Bureau meetings and other gatherings she told other farm wives her experiences with electricity on the farm. Farm and electrical magazines published her articles and radio stations began to broadcast interviews with her.

Lehmann's group kept detailed data on the way the women on the ten farms used their time. Soon it became clear that electric washing machines and vacuum cleaners alone were saving each housewife as much as ten hours a week, leaving more time for gardening, poultry raising, and other profit-making activities.

But the data revealed an interesting side effect: the number of hours the women spent on personal grooming increased in every case, and almost doubled in one instance. This unexpected development resulted from increased leisure time and social contact, the latter brought on partly by the study itself, which required frequent visits to the farm homes by the investigators. "You need to look prettier for a man from the University than you do for the chickens," one of the Tolono women said.

Lehmann also used the farms as testing areas for experimental electrical equipment that had come out of the farm mechanics, agronomy, and other laboratories. Tests at various research centers had already established that egg production could be increased with controlled lighting by as much as 21 per cent during the winter months when prices were high. Poultry house lighting with automatic time switches could lengthen the chicken's day to 12 or 13 hours; the 40-watt bulbs served as artificial suns to rouse the sleeping chickens while it was still dark outside. The Tolono experiments bore out the earlier findings and introduced the system to Illinois.

The Tolono experiment indicated beyond any doubt that there was a place for electricity on the farm. On the ten test farms, only draft horses and tractors played a greater role than electricity in supplying energy. Energy and time tables compiled for farmstead equipment showed that the highest monthly total averaged 278 kilowatt-hours; the lowest, 42. This compared with an average monthly household consumption in the cities of 50 kilowatt-hours.

The task of expanding the applications of electricity on the farms now lay before the researchers, but there could be no electrical appliances without electricity. A means had to be found to make electricity available to the farmers at a price they would be willing and able to pay. Lehmann devoted a six-month sabbatical leave from the University to working out equitable electric rates with the Central Illinois Public Service Company in Springfield. Armed with the indisputable results of his Tolono experiment, he was eventually able to convince the power companies that there was a tremendous potential for electric power on the farms—in fact, a much larger per capita market than in the cities.

Lehmann won a number of rate concessions from the major utilities, but it soon became apparent that these would not be sufficient to do the job he wanted. If most Illinois farmers were to have electric power, a broader, more positive program, geared especially to the farms and their problems of distance and scattered population, would have to be provided.

At the end of the Tolono experiment, rural electrification seemed almost as far away as it had at the beginning. The great value of the experiment lay in the fact that many farmers had become aware of the potential of electric power for their work. County Farm and Home Bureau representatives and members of other farm organizations worked with the University Extension representatives to bring the story of the Tolono successes to every rural community in the state. Farmers themselves began seeking information. Studies of a similar nature in other state universities were making the issue of farm electrification a national concern. It became evident that, if the rural segment of the population were ever to have electrical power, the issue would have to be supported by someone other than the power companies. The farm interest groups turned from the utilities in the early 1930's and headed toward Washington, where they hoped their arguments would receive more attention.

In the fall of 1935, six years after the Tolono test ended, President Franklin D. Roosevelt issued an Executive Order establishing the Rural Electrification Administration. Set up to subsidize the utilities and thereby encourage their extension into the rural areas, the program proved to be ineffective and unpopular with the power companies, and participation was negligible. Nevertheless, the people who had struggled for so many years for a comprehensive program of rural electrification took heart.

The farm lobbies regrouped for a battle with Congress the following year. In the legislative hopper was a bill entitled the Rural Electrification Act of 1936. It had been drawn up by the Vice-President of the United States in consultation with the president of the National Federation of Farm Bureaus and the president of the Illinois Agriculture Association. Illinois, one of the most progressive and prosperous of the farm states, had long been recognized in Washington as a leader in the fight for rural electrification legislation. Spearheading the Illinois effort was Lehmann's own Champaign County Farm Bureau.

Victory came early in the session. On May 20, 1936, the Rural Electrification Act was signed into law by President Roosevelt. It would be one of the most permanent and successful acts to come out of the New Deal. Under the program, the Rural Electrification Administration would make available 35-year loans at two per cent interest to farmers wishing to work together to extend lines to their property. These systems would be controlled, operated, and jointly owned by the participating farmers. In the spring of 1936, when the REA began, approximately 16 per cent of rural America had access to electrical power. Thirty years and hundreds of millions of dollars later the number had climbed to over 98 per cent.

The coming of electric power to the farms was the catalyst which triggered the agricultural revolution. Radical changes and improvements in machinery, crop production, soil and water conservation, farm buildings, and home improvements followed almost immediately. Agricultural engineers suddenly saw their world become a universe. At Illinois the Department of Farm Mechanics was incorporated into the College of Engineering as the Department of Agricultural Engineering.

In 1938, as the first tangible results of the Rural Electrification Act were manifesting themselves over rural America, President Roosevelt delivered a speech at Barnesville, Georgia. In the course of his address he spoke of his first visit to his retreat in Warm Springs, Georgia:

> There was only one discordant note in that first stay of mine at Warm Springs. When the first-of-the-month bill came in for electric light for my little cottage, I found that the charge was 18 cents a kilowatt hour—about four times what I pay at Hyde Park, New York. That started my long study of public utility charges for electric current and the whole subject of getting electricity into farm homes. . . . So it can be said that a little cottage at Warm Springs, Georgia, was the birthplace of the Rural Electrification Administration.

An important and farsighted piece of legislation may well have been born in the little cottage at Warm Springs, as President Roosevelt stated; but many of the ideas and much of the inspiration behind it had their origins elsewhere—such as in the minds of men like Emil Lehmann.

THE FAILURE THAT SUCCEEDED

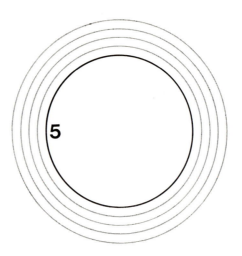

5

A fourteen-car passenger train slowed to 25 mph in antici-
pation of a trestle on an August evening in 1911. Its destina-
tion, the village of Manchester, New York, was scarcely ten
minutes away. Suddenly the third car of the train lurched
violently from the track and plunged headlong into a river
40 feet below. The remaining cars followed in deafening
succession. Although it was not the first of the mysterious
derailments, the results were unusually tragic: 29 persons were killed and twice that number injured. Pieces
of a faulty rail believed to have been responsible were
rushed to Washington for an investigation by the Interstate
Commerce Commission. After months of research, engi-
neer-physicist James E. Howard reported that the cause of
the accident could be traced to "transverse fissures and
longitudinal seams in the head of the rail." The verdict was
a frightening one, implicating over 300,000 miles of rails
already in service. The Commerce Commission issued an
urgent appeal that "exhaustive scientific inquiry" be undertaken to determine why and how such failures occurred.

For two decades the railroads and the steel mills sought

to solve the fissure enigma with little success. Their only tangible progress was in the perfection of a detector car, invented by Elmer A. Sperry, the famed inventor who pioneered in gyroscopes for navigation and guidance. The Sperry car rolled over rails finding fissures or "rail cancers," as Sperry called them, before they revealed themselves with disastrous consequences.

Twelve thousand rails failed each year in the United States and Canada, often resulting in derailments and the loss of lives and property. In an era in which 70 per cent of all freight was carried by rail, the fissure problem was a national concern. To add to the dilemma, more powerful engines pulling heavier cargoes were increasing the frequency of failures. Something had to be done.

In 1929 Professor Herbert F. Moore of the Theoretical and Applied Mechanics Department at Illinois was concluding a ten-year investigation of the fatigue of metals. The extensive study had brought the fifty-five-year-old mechanical engineer recognition as the foremost authority in his field. For the last two years of that investigation the rail fissures question had intrigued him. Under his direction a laboratory rail fatigue tester had been designed and constructed, and minor fissure tests were being carried out. Funds were dwindling, however, and the fatigue investigation was nearing a close. Department head Melvin Enger told Moore he might possibly come up with $8,000 to extend the rail study for another year, but he was not optimistic: it was the beginning of the Depression years and research money was scarce.

In the spring of 1930 a delegation from the Rail Manufacturers' Technical Committee and the American Railway Engineering Association visited Moore at the University of Illinois. His reputation in metals research was quite familiar to them. During the past ten years he had written two books, published scores of articles, and lectured all over the United States and in Europe. The delegation's interest in his work was more specific: after 20 years of fruitless attempts, they wanted a solution to the rail fissures mystery. Perhaps this white-haired man with the ink stains on his tie could give it to them. They were willing to pay—$50,000 a year for five years.

Moore sat back in his chair, facing the men. "We'll try anything once," he said. He knew, though, that it would take many tries—perhaps thousands. Neither he nor his visitors could know that ten years, not five, would pass before the ultimate solution was found.

The delegation had come to the University of Illinois to talk to Moore, yet their decision had been influenced by other factors. The University had become involved in rail-

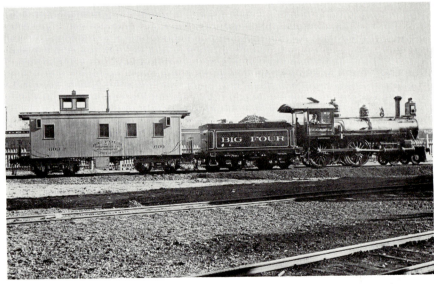

Dynamometer cars such as No. 609, used to measure the power output of a locomotive in service, were developed by the University in conjunction with the Big Four Railroad.

road research early in its history. In 1898, the Department of Mechanical Engineering initiated a series of railway engineering courses, a curriculum so popular that it grew into the Department of Railway Engineering a few years later. The railroad associations had extended their support to the University, making excellent research equipment and facilities available.

The University had acquired a locomotive laboratory where a full-sized locomotive could be run at full speed on a treadmill system of rollers. Studies were begun in which wheels were run on rails in experiments that duplicated the wear of actual railroading. The rails themselves were put through thousands of hours of fatigue testing on specially designed machines. Over the years this work had earned the University an excellent reputation with the railroad associations.

In addition, Arthur N. Talbot, recently retired head of the Department, had just completed the final report on an "Investigation of Stresses in Railroad Track," a 17-year study of the effects of moving locomotives and cars on tracks. Many experts considered the findings the most signif-

Some of the noisiest research ever conducted on the campus began in 1912. Engines were run at high speed on a series of rollers in the locomotive testing laboratory, duplicating the conditions of actual operation.

icant contribution to the scientific knowledge of railroads ever made.

During the summer and fall of 1930, materials and equipment for the new investigation accumulated rapidly. The year-old Materials Testing Laboratory was beginning to look like a rail yard by September. Carloads of rails and wheels were arriving daily.

Moore had the equipment and the money. He knew he also had the men—men like Howard Thomas, who as his engineer of tests would be his first lieutenant. In the early days of the rail stress investigation, "Tommy" had proved himself to be a perfectionist. His meticulousness would be a valuable asset in overseeing the laboratory investigations and in drawing conclusions from the data. N. H. Roy had already shown his abilities in the metal fatigue investigation. As supervisor of field studies, he would concentrate his efforts on the effects of wheel loads on rail fissures. Ralph Cramer was new to the University, a metallurgist hired especially for the investigation to conduct metallurgical and chemical tests. In all, 19 of them were starting out on the investigation; twelve engineers, six technicians, and one secretary.

Besides men, money, and equipment, Moore had another resource on his side—a strong conviction that the investigation would succeed. A devout Congregationalist, Moore often had said that progress could be measured with a yardstick in the engineering world, but in life you had to rely on faith to know if you were headed in the right direction. In the years to come, he would at times rely as heavily on the latter as the former.

But Moore needed a peg on which to hang the investigation. Previous research in laboratories throughout the country had suggested that shatter cracks, microscopic cracks imbedded in the rail head, might be the nuclei from which the fissures grew. This assumption would be the starting point.

In the following months, rails were sliced and their cross sections etched with acid. Shatter cracks showed up as minute flaws in the otherwise solid rails. These samples, as well as uncracked specimens, were then subjected to hundreds of thousands of cycles of rolling weight in a fatigue testing machine developed by Moore during his metal fatigue investigation. This machine subjected rails to loads like those of actual trains. The tests were accelerated, however, and specimens were pulled back and forth under the wheel load 55 times a minute; the weight of the load could be varied from zero to 80,000 pounds. Hundreds of rails were etched, about one-fourth of which were found to contain shatter cracks. Rolling-load tests on both categories

Tests revealed that fissures grew from tiny imperfections called shatter cracks which formed in the rails during processing.

of rails revealed an interesting fact—although not all rails with shatter cracks developed fissures under fatigue testing, all that developed fissures had shatter cracks.

Many times Moore conducted the tests himself, arriving in the lab at 7:00 A.M. and descending to the testing bay in a gray lab coat. This was his favorite part of the day, for he prided himself on being a practical engineer who knew "which side of his hands to get dirty." He knew that somebody had to coordinate the work of the machinists with the engineers and the steel and railroad representatives, but he wanted to be involved with all phases of the tests, too.

Soon the accumulating data definitely implicated shatter cracks as the culprit in the fissures investigation. But the acceptance of one piece of knowledge at this early stage raised more questions than it answered. What caused some cracks to expand into fissures while others remained dormant? How large a repeated load did it take to shatter a rail? Which was more dangerous to a shatter-cracked rail— the force of the wheel itself, or the bending leverage such a force exerted on the rail? These were important questions, yet they were only exploratory research problems, symptoms to be diagnosed before an actual cure could be considered.

In short, the project needed information. Testing was the only way to get it. According to Moore, "No question appeared more important in this investigation than the question of proper tests for detecting a shatter-cracked condition in a rail." Finding the right nondestructive test was the responsibility of Norville J. Alleman and Joseph L. Bisesi.

By 1936 several types of destructive tests were being used. Drop tests involved letting a 2,000-pound weight fall freely from a height of 20 feet onto a rail. Theoretically, one blow of this type would be sufficient to produce failure if the tested rail contained shatter cracks. In actual practice, results were less positive and many flawed rails were still intact after several blows. Such tests suffered two disadvantages: first of all, they were imprecise, since energy loads increased in 40,000-foot-pound jumps and it was impossible to derive the precise load at which a rail would shatter; and secondly, the strain readings after all blows but the first were inaccurate because measurements were distorted in the bent and twisted rails.

The bend test, proposed by the Pennsylvania Railroad and the Illinois Steel Company, was more sensitive than the drop test. The five- or six-foot rail was bent in a hydraulic press. The pressure of the load and the deflection of the rail at fracture were graphically recorded on an attached revolving drum. This was the test the project came to rely upon most heavily, although Alleman was never satisfied with it.

The etch test was an accurate and thorough method of detecting shatter cracks, but it required cutting out large samples and could not show a pattern for the entire rail. Since it failed to indicate the forces necessary to induce fissures from the shatter cracks, neither was it a quantitative test. Though not perfect by any means, the etch test was fast and accurate as far as it went, and it came to play an important part in the investigation.

All of these destructive tests had a common fault. They had to be applied to samples rather than to a general rail population, and the results were therefore not truly representative. Moore urged Alleman to continue with his research in hopes of producing a satisfactory nondestructive test to detect shatter cracks. In the months and years to follow, Alleman and Bisesi tried and rejected scores of tests which used amplified microphones, electrical resistance, magnetic field distortion, and sound waves. Meanwhile research continued using the destructive bend and etch tests.

By 1934 Thomas and his laboratory crew had established that wheel load rather than flexural stress triggered the development of fissures from shatter-crack nuclei. Once the fissures had begun, however, flexural stress determined their direction and extent. Laboratory research further indicated that the wheel load necessary to start fissures could be as low as 40,000 pounds, depending upon the size and location of the shatter cracks. But 40,000 pounds, Moore knew, was considerably greater than the load under a wheel of even the heaviest freight car. Had they been mistaken?

Moore recalled a report by Talbot on the early rails investigation. In the report Talbot had concluded that certain inertia forces caused by flat spots on wheels, track surface irregularities, out-of-round wheels, etc., could increase the effective weight of car wheels.

To verify Talbot's conclusions in terms of the present investigation, Moore dispatched road crews directed by Thomas and Roy to measure the wheel loads in service on tracks. During an eight-week study they took readings on 500,000 wheel loads in four states. The results showed that about one wheel load in a thousand exerted 40,000 pounds of force or more. Talbot had been right.

In another area of the investigation, the effect of sub-zero temperatures on rails was studied with the cooperation of the U.S. Army Air Corps in Dayton, Ohio. There were scores of other such specialized studies, including investigations of fissures in Bessemer steel rails and the formation of longitudinal fissures. Hopefully these would provide clues to the general behavior of the fissures and shatter cracks.

At times the men grew discouraged with results which failed to back up their theories, results which contradicted months or even years of research. "A negative result to me is every bit as conclusive as a positive result," Moore emphasized. "We wouldn't be testing if we knew what we wanted to find."

As data steadily mounted from laboratory and field investigations, efforts were being made to trace the failures back to their source—the steel mills. The final solution would, of necessity, center on steel processing, but locating the answer amid the mass of collected data was proving to be quite a task.

It was a task which Moore knew must ultimately fall to the metallurgical and chemical section of the investigation.

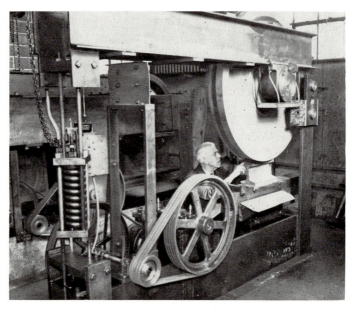

Moore himself conducted many of the tests to determine the load capacity of rails.

During the early years, the only noteworthy chemical tests were fruitless attempts to link nitrogen and oxygen with the presence of shatter cracks. Most of the metallurgists' time was divided between touring steel mills to observe casting and cooling techniques and photographing the minute shatter cracks under microscopes in the laboratory. So far their only tangible results were thousands of neatly labeled photographs.

One morning Moore arrived at work to find Ralph Cramer, director of the metallurgical tests, waiting for him. The stocky, sandy-haired metallurgist nervously tapped a rolled copy of a technical magazine against the palm of his hand as he waited for Moore to unlock his office door and hang up his overcoat. Cramer often brought articles he had read to Moore's attention, but this morning he was excited. Moore quickly learned why: the article presented a hypothesis that hydrogen was present in flaked or shatter-cracked rails. It was written by I. C. Mackie, a metallurgist for a Nova Scotian steel mill. Here was an exciting new clue for the investigation, an avenue which needed to be explored.

Moore immediately instructed Cramer to begin research into the hydrogen hypothesis. To verify the conclusions of the Canadian observations, Cramer ordered that shatter-crack-free rails be reheated in an atmosphere of hydrogen gas in a University of Illinois shop laboratory furnace. Etch tests were then made to determine whether shatter cracks had developed. Of the seven rails tested, all but two had sprouted elaborate networks of shatter cracks. Similar results from European tests indicated that they were on the right track—"a good place to be in a rails investigation," Moore punned.

This was the start of the three-year study of hydrogen in steel rails which would eventually solve the fissures mystery. Progress was gratifyingly fast—like slipping the final dozen pieces into a jigsaw puzzle. Further testing at Illinois and in the steel mills showed that molten steel would absorb more than its own volume of hydrogen from the water vapor and combustion products of the furnace atmosphere. During cooling some of the gas would escape, but much of it remained trapped inside the steel. The remaining hydrogen would then collect around impurities within the rail. When enough molecules had gathered in one place, the pressure would increase and result in shatter cracks.

Cramer believed that the hydrogen became trapped

when the steel cooled to a critical temperature near 400°F, at which point the hydrogen could not diffuse fast enough to escape. Therefore, he reasoned, the cooling process had to be slowed enough to allow the hydrogen molecules adequate time to escape before the critical temperature was reached. The first tests of this theory were carried out under Cramer's direction in 1937 at the Tennessee Coal, Iron & Fuel Company in Birmingham, Alabama. Rails were slowly cooled in insulated wooden boxes. Test results indicated that the critical temperature was not 400 degrees, as previously supposed, but somewhere between 200 and 300 degrees.

Other tests indicated that slow cooling at high temperatures enabled the hydrogen to escape so that there was no gas to form shatter cracks when the critical temperature was reached. In addition, specimens cooled from 900 to 200 degrees in less than four hours developed shatter cracks. Moore had established to his own satisfaction that "control-cooling," as the process came to be known, held the solution to the problem. Testing continued during 1938 and the early months of 1939 at the Dominion Steel and Coal Corporation in Sydney, Nova Scotia, where the hydrogen idea had originated, and at the Gary mill of the Carnegie-Illinois Steel Corporation. Much of Moore's time as well as Cramer's was divided between these two laboratories.

To make sure that the control-cooling method would actually stop shatter cracks in regular rails, experiments were made on rails which had been seeded with hydrogen while they were being manufactured. If the engineers could eliminate shatter cracks in these rails, they could eliminate them from any. Cramer felt that by interrupting the cooling process at a temperature well above the critical point, all hydrogen could be released and shatter cracks prevented without lowering the quality of the steel. For the test, hydrogen-treated rails were placed in a furnace at each of two different temperatures, 1100 and 900 degrees Fahrenheit. A single specimen was removed every hour and air cooled from this supercritical temperature. Etching showed that the rails held at the higher temperature for three hours or longer did not develop shatter cracks; also, those held at 900 degrees for four hours or longer developed no cracks. But every rail which was air-cooled quickly from the high temperatures contained over 100 shatter cracks.

Moore and his group had done it—or at least laboratory tests said they had. The real laboratory, of course, stretched across a continent. By September, 1939, over two million tons of the control-cooled rails had been laid. Every mill in the country had adopted the process. In that year over 30,000 conventionally made rails which were still in service developed fissures. Not one of the control-cooled rails developed a shatter crack or a fissure. The researchers waited, running hundreds of faulty rails through their testing devices to determine if there was a flaw in their theory. Years passed and their findings were always the same: no shatter cracks, no fissures.

The investigation was a success. Elimination of the dangerous rail cancer saved the railroads over 100 million dollars, a savings which would accumulate at the rate of nine million dollars a year. Railroad officials enthusiastically hailed the University of Illinois for solving the rail mystery. To much of the technical world the University became identified as the savior of the railroad industry. However, for the men who had worked on the investigation since its beginning, theirs was in many ways a triumph without victory. At least half of the credit, and perhaps more, rightfully belonged to an obscure engineer hidden away in a Nova Scotian steel mill. In retrospect it was obvious that too much of the University's time and effort had been directed to rail fatigue (the effect) and too little to the chemical and metallurgical failings in the steel (the cause). Nevertheless, University engineers had established the control-cooling method which made it possible to produce hydrogen-free rails without costly revisions in the steel-rolling process.

Whether or not the role of hydrogen could have been identified without Mackie's preliminary work cannot be determined; whether Mackie's idea would have been developed without the University of Illinois is likewise a moot question. But unfortunately injustice clouded a brilliant cooperative success. Although his was perhaps the most important single contribution of the entire project, Mackie was almost forgotten as the railroads credited the solution of the problem wholly to the University of Illinois.

ELECTRONS IN ORBIT

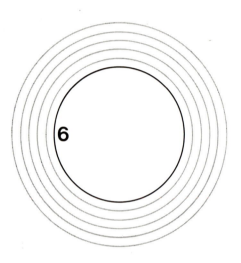

6

The Depression hit the University of Illinois late, but it hit hard. In his 1934–35 annual report to engineering Dean Melvin Enger, Physics Department head Wheeler Loomis said: "The department, whose operating expenses have been reduced to a starvation point for over three years, suffered a financial crisis this winter and pretty nearly had to close up. It was rescued, temporarily, by the allotment of $2,200 from general and engineering funds. . . . It is almost impossible to convey an adequate idea of the extent to which our work, both in teaching and research, has been hampered. . . ."

Among Loomis's problems was that of hiring new men. As late as 1936, he was forced to eliminate potential staff members whose wives were employed and were already earning grocery money. He failed to hire I. I. Rabi and Hans Bethe, two physicists who would become internationally known for their work in nuclear physics, because he was short of each man's salary requirements by just a few hundred dollars.

Despite his department's poverty, Loomis was able to

hire two young men who would do important work at Illinois. Twenty-seven-year-old Donald Kerst was an aggressive young experimenter whose intuitive understanding of the magnetic properties of iron gave him a reputation for knowing "more about how iron feels than any other man alive."

Robert Serber, who had been recommended for a position at Illinois by Robert Oppenheimer, was an outstanding theoretician in particle physics. Serber and Kerst got along well on the research program they soon began because both were quiet, friendly, and aggressive about their work.

They had more spirit than money. In 1939 the Graduate School granted them $400 to build an electron accelerator to smash atoms. Even this small sum was granted reluctantly because success in the project looked so unlikely to Univerity officials.

Their pessimism seemed justified. Such famous scientists as Planck, Einstein, and Heisenberg had uncovered a great deal of information on the nature of the atom's outer structure, but had learned little about its nucleus. Atoms of radioactive elements like radium and uranium, however, disintegrated spontaneously, revealing their inner composition. Could the nuclei of stable elements be similarly shattered? From this question came the idea of bombarding atoms with subatomic "bullets" to tear them apart. Such "bullets" would require "guns"—particle accelerators.

The first of these was the cyclotron, invented at the University of California by Ernest O. Lawrence. The cyclotron accelerated the heavier nuclear particles—protons—in a spiraling orbit within a magnetic field until they had gained sufficient energy to smash atoms. The second cyclotron ever built was constructed at Illinois in 1936.

But many experiments required the lighter particles—electrons—as ammunition. By the late 1930's American, English, and German physicists had tried to build accelerators that would hold electrons in stable circular orbits. But one problem had stopped them all. No one had managed to create a magnetic field which would simultaneously accelerate the electrons and hold them in orbit. Thus the chances of success, even for the young man supposed to know most about "how iron feels," looked slim.

The design Kerst and Serber settled upon operated like a common transformer, in which an alternating electric current in a coil of wire induces a current to flow in a second coil. In the accelerator the second coil of wire would be replaced by a doughnut-shaped hollow tube evacuated of air. Instead of flowing along a wire, the electrons would orbit within this tube. Held in orbit by a large magnet and accelerated by a changing magnetic field extending through the center of the tube, the electrons would gain energy with every revolution until they approached the speed of light. Then they would be released to hit a target, producing high-energy X rays that could be brought out of the machine in a straight, piercing beam. As an alternative, the electrons themselves could be taken from the machine as a high-energy beam.

In 1939, nine months after Kerst's arrival at Illinois, Wheeler Loomis reported that "Instructor D. W. Kerst has this year invented, designed, and nearly completed the construction of a very bold and original device for accelerating electrons to energies of millions of volts. He and all of us realize that it is a very long shot to hope that this device will be successful since it is so original and so different from anything previously attempted. . . . If it succeeds it will be of really extraordinary importance since one cannot see in advance any limit to the voltages that can be obtained with this device. If it fails he will just have to forget about it, but . . . he is obviously an experimentalist of great talent."

Early the next year the accelerator, named the "betatron," began to take shape. Kerst named it from the Greek letter "beta," used in science as a symbol for electron, and "tron," meaning "an instrument for." A German friend suggested another title: "Ausserordentlichhohegeschwindigkeitselektronentwickelndenschwerarbeitsbeigollitron," which translates roughly as, "Hard working by golly machine for generating extraordinarily high-velocity electrons."

A more serious problem facing Kerst was that of constructing a vacuum tube shaped like a doughnut with two arms. These arms would hold the device to inject the electrons, the target for the electrons to strike at the end of their orbits, and the ground wire connection. The first tubes built leaked badly. After months of failures Kerst concluded a report with cheerful irony: "Trials will continue."

Kerst and Serber managed to patch the leaking tubes enough to make them work, and with the rest of their $400, plus whatever equipment they were able to beg, borrow, or steal, they finished the machine.

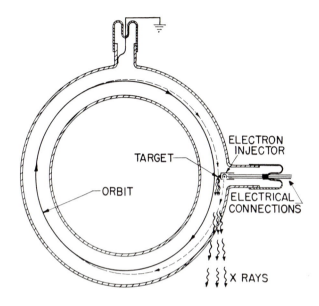

On July 15, 1940, the betatron was switched on for the first time. It worked. Kerst had accomplished what other scientists around the world had not: the magnetic field he designed held the electrons in a circle of constant diameter, even though their energy increased with each orbit, and forced errant electrons back into the equilibrium orbit. But to Kerst the guide field was only a necessary step in the design of the accelerator.

Moments after the machine began to operate he phoned his fiancée and held the receiver near the Geiger counter. When she heard the clicking caused by the betatron's radiation, the future Mrs. Kerst said, "It's the most beautiful noise I've ever heard." She hoped that the machine's success would let him now find a little time away from physics. Next Kerst wired department head Wheeler Loomis, who was vacationing in Massachusetts, "It works!"

Two days later Loomis received a letter which began: "No doubt the telegram I sent you two nights ago said all too little about my results. This letter should do better. Monday afternoon the electron accelerator started to work. . . . The electrons actually succeeded in going 60 miles to the target. Measurements of maximum field strength were made so that the energy could be computed, and it turns out to be 2 million volts." The last line of the letter read, "It seems too good to be true that the experiment is working just about like the calculations said it would."

The betatron did work as the calculations had predicted. Electrons were injected with 1,500 volts of energy. They traveled 200,000 revolutions (about 60 miles), gaining up to 25 electron-volts of energy per turn. They then hit the target, producing 2.3-million-electron-volt X rays. All this, from injection to emergence, took 1/2500 of a second. The 200-pound machine was only three feet long, one foot high, and one foot wide.

Donald Kerst, the inventor of the betatron, makes an adjustment on the original machine.

But this machine was really just a working model of the accelerator Kerst wanted. He felt that to be really useful a betatron would have to produce at least 20-million-electron-volt X rays. In the fall of 1940 Kerst took a leave of absence from the University to work at General Electric. There the facilities he needed for the larger machine were available. He and the new Mrs. Kerst drove to Schenectady with the Mark I betatron in the trunk of their car. At GE he directed the construction of a 20-MeV betatron, which was later shipped back to Illinois. The 20-MeV betatron was installed in a corner of the Abbott Power Plant, not because of larger power requirements, but because it was the only space available. The betatron was put into operation on February 24, 1942.

The second machine was a good deal larger than the first. Instead of 200 pounds, it weighed four tons. The magnet itself weighed 7,000 pounds. In this machine the electrons were injected with 60,000 volts of energy and allowed to circle 330,000 times (250 miles). Twenty-million-electron-volt X rays were produced when the electrons hit the target. The target could be made so small that the X rays originated from it in an area no more than 1/100 inch in diameter, thus allowing sharper X-ray pictures to be produced than had been possible before. Such X rays were ideal for examining metal parts for flaws, since cracks as narrow as 5/1000 inch could be seen in metal 20 inches thick.

Kerst felt that the 20-MeV betatron was the ideal size for hospitals, since it had ample energy and was of reasonable dimensions. Although he pointed out that the machine was not yet ready for clinical use, he felt that it could become a first-line weapon for use in destroying malignant growths. He compared it to previous X-ray machines, whose effect was greatest on the surface and decreased as the rays passed into and through the body. The 20-MeV X rays were so penetrating that with cross-firing techniques the dosage could easily be built up at any point within the body to a level much greater than was received at any point on the surface.

Kerst had also devised a method by which an electron beam, instead of the X rays, could be led out of the betatron and applied directly in experiments or for medical purposes. Such an electron beam would have unique advantages in therapy. "At 20 million volts," Kerst said, "these electrons will penetrate as far as ten centimeters (about four inches) and no farther. Thus there is no damage beyond the area of treatment."

Medical tests of the betatron were first made at the University of Illinois College of Medicine in Chicago. The first betatron for medical use was installed in the University of Illinois Research Hospital, and other machines were built for hospitals across the country. Kerst's interest in the betatron as a medical tool was gathering support.

Even before the machine was installed at the Illinois Research Hospital a graduate student of the University became the first patient to be treated with a betatron. He had begun to experience fainting spells and loss of memory in late 1947. After the problem was diagnosed as a brain tumor, he underwent surgery in Chicago. The operation proved unsuccessful. In April, 1948, he was transferred to a hospital in Urbana, where the decision was made to give him radiation treatment with the betatron at the University. The doctors made this decision, although reluctantly, because they felt that the patient had no other chance to survive, and because the campus betatron was the only one available.

This mockup of a patient's head was used to focus the betatron's X-ray beam on the precise location necessary to treat a brain tumor.

Under the supervision of medical doctors, preparations for the treatments were made as swiftly as possible. Casts of the patient's head were taken and used to set the focus of the betatron's beam so that it would strike the precise area of the tumor when the patient was in place. Experiments to determine the effects of such high-energy radiation on animals were also conducted. On April 30 the first treatment was given, after which the patient's condition was slightly improved. He was treated each successive day through May 16, with continuing evidence that the tumor was being reduced. Generally, however, the patient was becoming weaker, and on May 16 the radiation treatments had to be stopped because of the patient's increasing infirmity. On May 30 he died.

Meanwhile Kerst, Serber, and others at Illinois continued to develop the accelerator. Kerst and Professor Gerald Almy applied themselves to the problem of making better vacuum tubes for the betatron. Previous tubes, made of many glass parts waxed together, had to be pumped constantly to maintain the required vacuum. Often they leaked too badly to be used. Almy and Kerst devised a system to evacuate and permanently seal the tubes if problems of construction and materials could be solved. The tubes' specifications were discussed with Ralph K. Hursh of the Ceramic Engineering Department, who set to work on the problem.

Finally a highly vacuum-tight porcelain with the proper thermal expansion and strength was developed. Tubes made from this porcelain, thinly coated with paladium on the inside and glazed on the outside, were put into production in the Ceramic Engineering Department. The result of this cooperative effort was "a tube that could be changed as easily as a light bulb" with far longer life than the earlier experimental "doughnuts."

Professors Hursh and Almy examine one of the vacuum tubes which were produced in the Ceramic Engineering Department for the betatron. A special vacuum-tight porcelain was developed for the tubes.

Kerst's plans for an even larger betatron were interrupted by the war. In 1942 Serber, whose theoretical work on the betatron had been invaluable, left Illinois to work on the atom bomb at Los Alamos. Major General Leslie Groves, chief of the Manhattan Engineering District, asked the University to allow Kerst to join his group at once "for a special job." Arthur Cutts Willard, President of the University, argued that Kerst's betatron work was more important to the war effort than any "special job." He found that during wartime a university president is no match for a general, and in the fall of 1943 Kerst, too, left to work on the atom bomb project.

Betatron research and development did not stop at Illinois during Kerst's temporary absence. Almy headed the research team that continued the development of the betatron for X-ray radiography of metal sections, with financial support from the Federal Office of Scientific Research and Development. Three 4-million-electron-volt betatrons were built in the Physics Department shops. One was sent to the Naval Research Laboratory in Washington, D.C., another to the Woolwich Arsenal in England, and the third remained at Illinois.

The growth of industrial uses for the betatron seemed to indicate its success. Betatron X rays were used to inspect massive steel breechblocks of artillery guns for flaws which might cause the weapons to explode in use. An improved 25-million-electron-volt betatron was also developed in cooperation with Allis-Chalmers. By the end of the war three of these machines were in use for radiography at Los Alamos, Rock Island Arsenal, and Picatinny Arsenal. After the war Allis-Chalmers built more than a dozen more of them for use in radiography, medical therapy, and scientific research.

Kerst returned to Illinois and resumed his plans for a mammoth betatron. In the spring of 1945, before the atomic bomb had been dropped and when money for any kind of research was extremely scarce, the members of the Illinois legislature showed their confidence in Kerst's machine by appropriating $1,500,000 to construct and house a large betatron.

Kerst immediately produced a design for an 80-MeV pilot model, which was completed and put into operation in 1948. Almost the same size and weight as the 20-MeV machine, its quadrupled power resulted from a much more sophisticated design made possible by the earlier research.

Kerst estimated, in fact, that if the same refinements could have been used in his original machine, the result would have been approximately as small as a penny match box.

As soon as the pilot model was finished, Kerst started to work on the big one—and it was big. With a design weight of 400 tons, this giant would fill a house. Its room in the new Physics Research Laboratory was so big that it was immediately nicknamed "the barn." Allis-Chalmers contracted to build the big betatron, and Kerst worked with the construction men from start to finish.

Building the world's largest betatron

One day during this period the President of the University and the Dean of the College of Engineering brought several distinguished guests to meet the famous Professor Kerst. When they arrived unannounced, Kerst's secretary, fearing the worst for her "sleeves-up" boss, wanted to warn him about his visitors. She called him on the intercom and said, "I'll be down to see you." His answer came back immediately: "Never mind—I'm coming up anyway. I'll be right there." Seconds later he bounded up the stairs in his undershirt and a layer of dirt. The red of his perspiring face deepened as he shook hands with the visitors.

The big betatron was completed in February, 1950. Kerst and University officials, unsure of the reliability of the giant accelerator, had prepared two news releases to describe the machine's trial run. One began, "The 300-MeV betatron of the University of Illinois, unveiled today, developed artificial cosmic rays 14 billion times as concentrated as those of nature. This betatron, like Kerst's first little 2½-MeV machine of ten years ago, operated on the first try. . . ."

The second announcement, less optimistic about the machine's adjustment, had stated, "First tests of the 300-MeV betatron of the University of Illinois were successful. Initial trials were made at part power. Full power tests will be made after the accelerator has been adjusted. . . ."

Dwarfed by the 300-MeV betatron, Kerst displays his original machine. The first betatron weighed 200 pounds; the giant accelerator, completed in 1950, 400 tons.

The first announcement was used. Like the first betatron, the new machine worked perfectly as soon as the switch was thrown. Electrons were injected with 100,000 electron-volts of energy to produce 300-million-electron-volt X rays. The main magnet, a construction achievement in itself, was 23 feet long, 13 feet high, and more than 6 feet thick. It was the largest betatron in the world. This machine differed from its predecessors in that the magnetic field which accelerated the electrons could be controlled in such a way as to give the electrons a much longer, stronger push, raising their speed and making the high energies possible.

But the importance of the betatron, which had grown so impressively in less than ten years, began to wane. Although high-energy radiation as a medical technique continued to be of great interest, betatrons began to be replaced for such purposes by a by-product of atomic bomb research, radioactive cobalt, which was smaller, quieter, and less expensive.

For industrial radiography, too, other X-ray sources began to displace the betatron. The last betatron put on the market was a 40-MeV version of the Allis-Chalmers model. Science and industry demanded more powerful and versatile accelerators, and higher-energy betatrons were not feasible for two reasons. The first was the tremendous size of the magnet required to provide the accelerating "push." The second reason was related to the fact that the electrons radiate energy as they travel through the doughnut. The higher the energy of an electron, the more energy it radiates away as it moves in its circular path. This characteristic requires a continually increasing amount of energy from the accelerator to hold the electron in orbit. The effect can be decreased by making the orbit radius larger, but this again increases the amount of iron required for the magnet.

Existing betatrons were still useful for many kinds of experiments, but by the early 1960's Kerst acknowledged that for future development the machine was "as dead as a dodo."

While the machine he developed has reached the limit of its usefulness, an accomplishment Kerst had regarded as almost routine would have far greater importance. The magnetic guide field would be incorporated into later, more powerful accelerators such as the gigantic Brookhaven and the Stanford linear accelerators. Few of the physicists associated with those machines would dispute that Kerst did indeed "know more about how iron feels than any other man alive."

THE IMPOSSIBLE ANTENNA

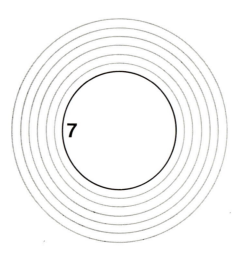

In 1954 Victor Rumsey may have been the only antenna engineer in the United States who really believed that the frequency-independent antenna was possible.

It was an important problem. Man's use of electromagnetic waves had altered his world and showed indications of altering it further. Entertainment, rapid communications, and warfare had been tremendously affected by developments such as radio, radar, and television—and how well these inventions worked depended upon their antennas.

Simply defined, an antenna is a device to transform an electric signal into an electromagnetic wave which will travel through air or space to a receiving antenna which collects and reconverts it into an electric signal. Household television antennas, for example, transform the electromagnetic waves broadcast from the television station back into an electric signal that the home TV set can use to reconstruct the sound and picture.

Most characteristics of sending and receiving antennas are identical. The signals broadcast from one kind of antenna to the other can be partially characterized by their frequencies. The current in the transmitting antenna alternates, flowing first in one direction and then in the other (a cycle), reversing many times a second with a given frequency. The wave produced has the same frequency, and as it travels through space each cycle of the wave has a specific size, called a wavelength.

Different frequencies are used for different transmitters, and an ordinary antenna can transmit efficiently only a very small range of frequencies (a narrow bandwidth). Bandwidths are usually measured in terms of the highest and lowest frequencies the antenna can transmit, and the ratio between these extremes is called the "bandwidth ratio."

Even by the end of World War II, the bandwidth ratio for most of the antennas in use was less than two to one. Many different kinds of antennas were built, each quite limited in the frequencies it could transmit or receive. What was needed were antennas with bandwidth ratios of 20 to 1 or better, so that one antenna could receive (or transmit) a wide range of signals.

Few experts in the field believed that such an antenna could be built. They knew that the characteristics of any antenna depend upon its size. The smaller the elements of an antenna, the higher the frequencies it can broadcast or receive. Its bandwidth cannot ordinarily be widened by simply adding elements of other sizes: the interference of the elements may, in fact, render the antenna useless.

The military need for better antennas had brought the University of Illinois into this aspect of electronics in 1948. The first project of the new Antenna Laboratory was research on antennas for high-speed aircraft. The small, ill-equipped laboratory was operated by only one professor and two graduate students—but it was a beginning.

By 1954 the Laboratory staff had only two full-time members—director Edward C. Jordan, who was leaving to head the Electrical Engineering Department, and Raymond H. DuHamel, a bright student who had received his Ph.D. in electrical engineering at Illinois just a year earlier. Jordan, realizing that his new job would leave DuHamel as the only full-time staff member in the Antenna Lab, began looking for a man to replace himself. The man he found was Victor Rumsey.

Before he came to Illinois, Rumsey had been the director of antenna research at Ohio State. While negotiating for a position on the West Coast he was invited to come to Illinois.

He agreed to stop at Illinois until the negotiations were completed. His "stop" would be more permanent than he had guessed.

When he arrived in Urbana, Rumsey saw one possibility for a frequency-independent antenna which would not violate the necessary relationship between the dimensions of an antenna and the wavelength of its signal. He felt that an antenna that reproduced itself under "scaling"—that was designed so that any section of it shared the proportions of any other section—would behave in the same way for all frequencies. His idea meant that the structure would have to be defined entirely by angles instead of lengths, because it seemed to him that an antenna unrestricted by length would theoretically pick up signals of any wavelength—it would be frequency independent.

At the time a number of investigators were interested in spiral antennas. Rumsey was also interested in a particular type of spiral, the logarithmic spiral, which fit his scaling theory. His first official act in his new job was to ask a graduate student, John Dyson, to test an antenna built according to this concept.

The design that resulted had arms spiraling out from the center, growing wider and farther apart as they emerged. The main problem that Rumsey and Dyson faced was deciding whether and where the arms could end. The antenna was supposed to represent a length extending to infinity. Unable to work out a theoretical answer to this problem, they set to work building an antenna whose arms would be cut off at some arbitrary length. The two men could only wait and test the results.

By the spring of 1955 they had cut such a spiral from sheet metal and tested it. They found it to be largely frequency independent, for it could pick up signals of many wavelengths, even though its elements were cut off at an arbitrary length. Their enthusiasm was dampened by the fact that the antenna had a serious shortcoming: it radiated signals from both sides. They knew that in use it might have to be mounted with one side against a surface such as an aircraft fuselage where streamlining was important. The radiation pattern from this side would be spoiled by the metal fuselage, and the pattern on the other side would revert to frequency dependence. To eliminate this problem they had to make the flat spiral unidirectional, but they were hampered by their scant knowledge of why it worked in the first place. "It's a confusing bloody business," Rumsey said. The spiral seemed to have brought them to a dead end. Perhaps the "impossible" antenna had been built only to show that it was impractical.

DuHamel, who with two years' seniority was the Lab's "old timer," became involved in the discussions between Rumsey and Dyson. "What would happen," he asked, "if we went back to a basically triangular shape like the bow-tie antenna, but attempted to force it to radiate all frequencies by cutting slots in the edges?"

DuHamel built such an antenna, "straightening" Rumsey's spiral so that it assumed the shape of two opposed triangles. The area between the triangles' tips was the "feed point," the region at which the signals were fed to or taken from the antenna. DuHamel laid out curved teeth and slots along the edges of each triangle on the basis of Rumsey's angle theory, so that the slots became increasingly wider and farther apart with distance from the intersection of the triangles. He also designed the teeth and slots to be self-complementary: if the two triangles were rotated so that their sides touched, the teeth of one would fit exactly into the slots of the other. The engineers' calculations indicated that the self-complementary configuration was necessary to make the antenna work properly. Since it did work they believed they had been correct.

Logarithmic spiral   "Toothed bow tie"

DuHamel's "toothed bow tie" was essentially frequency independent in that it worked well at several different frequencies. It was named the "log-periodic" antenna. The men still did not fully understand why it worked, but it was broadband. Unfortunately, it had the same limitation as the equiangular spiral: it was not unidirectional.

Through the next year they began to understand the effects of the complex geometries involved in their antennas. But it was, as Rumsey had said, "a confusing bloody business." With better computers they might have been able to comprehend the shapes more completely, but such computers were not available—and the mathematical analyses were terribly involved. Study and experimentation finally showed that the self-complementary configuration was unnecessary. What was essential was the "logarithmic growth" of the antenna "teeth" with distance from the center or feed point. Such a pattern had followed coincidentally from the angle theory. Almost by accident the Antenna Laboratory engineers had produced a workable design with an unnecessary restriction which they now eliminated.

Dwight Isbell, although an undergraduate, was an ingenious researcher with several years of industrial experience in antennas when he joined the Laboratory. He was well qualified to continue the work when DuHamel left the University to become the Director of Antenna Research at Collins Radio Company.

The problem confronting Isbell was how to make the log-periodic antenna unidirectional. One day he was discussing this question with Paul Mayes, an antenna expert who had joined the Lab with Rumsey. Isbell had reasoned that the flat log-periodic antenna would radiate in only one direction if he destroyed its symmetry by adding more log-periodic elements to one side.

"Why not bend the two elements into a vee?" Mayes suggested. "It should radiate only out of the big end, just like a horn."

So Isbell bent the two triangles of DuHamel's flat antenna toward each other and began testing. The results were both pleasing and astonishing. The new antenna was unidirectional, and it remained frequency independent— but it radiated in the "wrong" direction.

As it turned out, it was fortunate that the bent version of the log-periodic antenna radiated toward the feed point rather than away from it. Had the signal gone in the opposite direction, as Mayes had predicted, it would have been disrupted by the metal structure of the antenna itself. The assumption that such antennas would not work unless they were flat was disproved. Although the efficiency of the antenna's reception was in no way impaired, it soon became obvious that the angle between the triangular arms was important to the proper operation of the antenna. Again the researchers didn't know precisely why.

Later in 1957 Dyson discovered that the flat log-spiral might be made unidirectional in the same way. He had

Conical logarithmic spiral

been investigating a structure that combined a flat spiral with that same spiral projected onto a cone. Finally it occurred to him that the combination was unnecessary, because the cone-shaped spiral had been doing most of the work anyway. He found that the conical antenna was unidirectional, again radiating most of its energy in the unexpected direction—off the tip of the cone.

Meanwhile, another man in the College was having antenna problems. Professor Harold Webb, who was in charge of a 28-foot dish antenna mounted on the roof of the Electrical Engineering Building, was not getting the reception he thought should be possible. The big dish, nicknamed the "Moonbeam Antenna," was designed to receive radio signals bounced off the moon from a transmitting antenna in Belmar, New Jersey. The signals, which took 2½ seconds to make the half-million-mile journey, furnished valuable information about the upper atmosphere, which they passed through going and coming. Although the transmitting power was 40,000 watts, calculations had shown that only a very small fraction of this was reflected from the moon in the direction of the Electrical Engineering Building. The dish antenna was "listening" for a signal of less than a millionth of a millionth of a watt—a very small signal indeed. In addition, the original antenna on the dish was frequency dependent and had to be replaced whenever Webb wanted to switch from one frequency band to another. Hoping to improve the efficiency of the dish antenna's reception and its flexibility, Webb went to the Antenna Laboratory for help.

Isbell was assigned to design and build a special log-periodic antenna for the big dish. It was installed in July, 1958. The radio signals caught by the dish were focused to this log-periodic element, which fed them down to the sensitive receiving apparatus in the building. After some modifications the new feed element worked splendidly, allowing the dish to pick up several bands. It was the first of many applications of the new log-periodic antenna.

Log-periodic antenna research was now advancing in industry as well as at the University. At Collins, DuHamel found that successful log-periodic antennas could be made from wire as well as from sheet metal. This change not only made such antennas easier and cheaper to make, but also extended their range of application because the wire structures could be built to operate in the commercially useful

In 1958 a special log-periodic antenna was installed to improve the versatility and sensitivity of the "Moonbeam Antenna," which was mounted on the roof of the Electrical Engineering Building.

short-wave band. This discovery triggered the idea that the antennas Dyson had built by wrapping the logarithmically tapering arms around a cone might also work if constant-diameter wires were used. Dyson tried this, and with its success the researchers learned that they could make practical approximations where they had previously believed exact dimensions essential.

At the University Isbell had built a new log-periodic

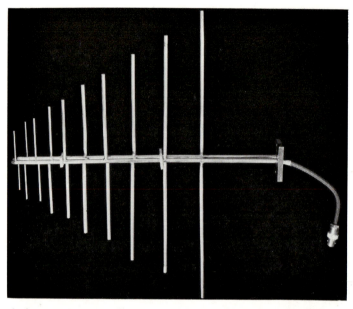

The log-periodic dipole was the first of the new antennas to use a criss-crossed connection of its elements.

shape—a dipole antenna array—with the antenna arms arranged perpendicularly across a backbone rod. The significant feature of Isbell's array was that the criss-crossed connection of the elements caused the antenna to "backfire," to radiate in the "wrong" direction as Isbell's vee-antenna had. This deviation from the conventional arrays, though not understood at the time, was later shown to be a necessary requirement of all log-periodic antennas. This antenna ultimately became one of the most popular of the broadband antennas.

During the next year Robert Carrel, a new graduate student, worked out a mathematical analysis of the log-periodic dipole array as a subject for his Ph.D. thesis. When published in October, 1960, the paper offered the first real information on designing such antennas. While it eliminated much of the cut-and-try effort of the work, it did not yet explain the fundamental reasons why log-periodic antennas were frequency independent.

During the same year Mayes and Carrel bent the perpendicular dipole arms of Isbell's antenna at vee-angles to the main backbone so that the structure resembled a fish skeleton. This antenna was designed to overcome one of the major shortcomings of the ordinary log-periodic dipole ar-

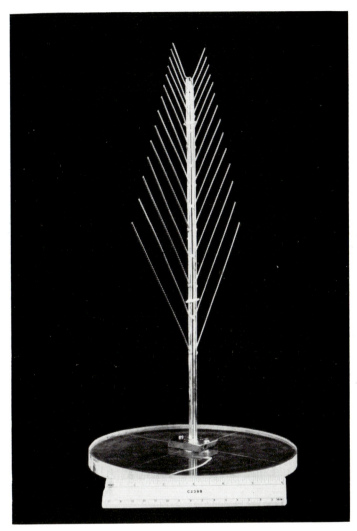

The search for a more compact antenna led to the development of the resonant-vee array.

ray—the extreme length of array required to cover several wide but separate bands of frequencies.

Within a few months a partial solution to the six-year-old mystery of how the antennas worked was published by Paul Mayes, Georges Deschamps, the new head of the Laboratory, and Willard Patton, a graduate student. The paper offered an approach through which the log-periodic antennas could be better understood. Freely interpreted, this definition suggested that the log-periodic antenna was a special composite structure made up of pieces of different antennas that individually could pick up only narrow parts of the entire frequency spectrum.

With this knowledge the researchers found that they could successfully design antennas to fit many new requirements. George Swenson, a professor of electrical engineering who had been working for several years on the design of a radio telescope, brought a large and difficult assignment to the Laboratory. The radio telescope Swenson had designed was giant—600 feet long and 400 feet wide—simple in concept and extremely ingenious. His plan was to reshape a natural ravine to serve as a curved "radio mirror," like the Moonbeam Antenna, to catch radio signals from the stars. Receiving antennas mounted on towers would be at the focal point of signals bounced from the mirror. These antennas would feed their signals to the receiving and recording equipment.

His design for a radio telescope would be relatively inexpensive to construct because it was a rigid structure, but this same rigidity would not allow it to scan the sky as many of the big movable-dish telescopes could. His question was: "If the radio telescope can be positioned so that scanning in the east-west direction will be accomplished by the earth's rotation, how can we make it scan from north to south?"

During 1960 the receiving antennas were completed. John Dyson had discovered that the north-south scanning required by Swenson could be accomplished simply by rotating log-spiral antennas a few degrees in order to cover a narrow arc of sky. Only one question remained: how should these antennas be placed for efficient operation?

The spacing and connection of the receiving antennas were important in receiving a narrow, pencil-shaped beam. This sharp beam was essential if the radio telescope was to "hear" the stars accurately. The antenna engineers specified the use of 276 of the log-spiral antennas. Their carefully calculated spacing not only worked to narrow the beam, but also reduced the number of elements required by more than one-third the number originally predicted. After the tests the radio telescope was put into operation on a five-year survey of radio sources beyond the Milky Way.

After all the years of work, complications, and misunderstandings, the log-periodic antennas were reasonably well understood, and had solved two serious problems at the University. They had also been used on the Atlantic and

The 600-foot-long radio telescope was designed to receive signals from the stars. Its parabolic reflector covers as much area as five football fields. An array of log-spiral antennas is mounted at the reflector's focus under the horizontal truss.

Pacific satellite tracking ranges, on satellites themselves, on moon probes, on military aircraft, and on ships. They had been developed to the point where they could receive bandwidth ratios of more than 40 to 1, and the entire development from "impossibility" to widespread use had taken place within ten years.

Most television antennas on the market when log-periodic antennas were conceived could effectively receive only one or two channels. By the summer of 1961 Paul Mayes and

The most successful and popular television antenna design is this array, a by-product of what began as military research at the University.

Robert Carrel had built log-periodic antennas that would pick up all channels, both VHF and UHF, ranging from channel 2 to channel 83.

It immediately became clear that these antennas would permit the reception of television signals in areas where it had been difficult to get any channel at all. Soon the log-periodic antenna was the most popular on the market, an interesting end-result of a research project originally conducted for the federal government.

Today the Antenna Laboratory has a spacious new home on the top floor of the Electrical Engineering Building. Professor Deschamps, the Laboratory's present director, says this of the discovery of the broadband antenna:

"I think the development of the log-periodic and log-spiral antennas was typical of how engineering often progresses. It had all the elements: the initial, simple, naked idea that provided the interest and motivation to do the work—the patient experimentation with its mixture of successes and failures—the guesses which turned out to be wrong but nevertheless led to new insights and understanding—the tools, theories, and methods of modern computing and physics—an interesting interaction of imaginative and creative individuals—and the long-awaited understanding of how the frequency-independent antennas worked—all these things were a part of it."

He adds: "We keep some of our past mistakes hanging around the Lab to remind us not to be too complacent in the future. We've also got several of the world's first frequency-independent antennas hanging out there."

A SILENT SOUND FOR SURGERY

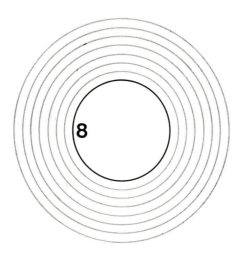

At 1:12 P.M. on March 21, 1958, the countdown began for the first ultrasonic "shot" into a human brain. Only the glow of a small light and the roll of numbers on an electronic timer indicated that a beam of sound was creating a tiny lesion—altering a few selected cells—deep within the man's brain. After one and one-half seconds of irradiation, the signal light darkened and the physician in charge asked the patient, "How do you feel?"

"All right."

At the doctor's side, William J. Fry felt tired, but relieved by the patient's reply. He had been working for five hours, calculating the required position and strength of the ultrasonic beam, and then guiding each step of the procedure with a special checklist. Nine more hours passed before he could relax—hours spent questioning the patient about his symptoms, checking them, making routine tests of his temperature, pulse, blood pressure, and reflexes, irradiating him again, and repeating the checking procedure. Finally the patient's skull was surgically closed, he was checked again, and the ordeal was over. The successful operation was an unusual landmark in the career of an unusual man.

Fry's career had an orthodox beginning. He was studying for his doctorate in physics when World War II broke out, interrupting his studies permanently. Fry went to work for the Naval Research Laboratory in Washington, D.C., where he earned a reputation for originality as a researcher. Because of this reputation, at the war's end he was offered a position in the University of Illinois' Electrical Engineering Department. The Department, planning to expand its research program, was less concerned with Fry's physics background than with his ability as an innovator.

He soon substantiated his reputation. Even before he arrived in Urbana Fry had begun plans for his research project: a powerful nuclear particle accelerator. Exhibiting a lack of concern that he came to be known for, he was unabashed by either the grand size or the novel circumstances of performing such a project—a physics project—within the Electrical Engineering Department.

Before his arrival at the University, Fry called Electrical Engineering Department head William L. Everitt, informing him of a Navy offer to give the University two powerful generators, valued at $250,000. The cost of this head start on the accelerator project would be the charges for shipping the machines from Washington to Urbana.

Before the generators were sent, however, the Physics Department reviewed Fry's proposal. Physics comprised part of the College of Engineering and the physicists, notably Donald Kerst and Robert Serber, the inventors of the betatron, were the University's resident accelerator experts. The Physics Department vetoed Fry's proposal as impractical. Seconding their veto was the shippers' estimate of the charges for delivering the generator units: $5,000. Fry was forced to change his plans.

Soon Fry succeeded in getting support for two projects related to his wartime work, one in infrared radiation and another on tunable sources for ultrahigh-frequency sound. His brother Frank, an electrical engineer who had worked on the atomic bomb project, joined him for the research. These initial projects were short-term studies, however, and as the work neared completion Fry began to look for more interesting, lengthy projects to tackle. For some time he had harbored an interest in the function of the brain and nervous system, an interest so foreign to his background in physics that he had not pursued it. Perhaps, he reasoned, there might be a way to combine his interests in a really substantial piece of research.

Fry began to survey the journals related to neurology. He found himself "surprised at how little was known quantitatively about the nervous system. In the physical systems I was accustomed to, the basic connections and interactions between parts were clear. But there seemed to be very little knowledge of this sort about the nervous system on the cellular level."

By the winter of 1947 Fry's initial projects were almost complete. He had been promoted to assistant professor, and had settled on a research topic: a general study of the central nervous system using high-frequency sound (ultrasonic) energy as a medium of exploration. The idea was completely new, and Fry had no idea what track the studies might take once they began. Everitt, although surprised by Fry's idea, agreed that he should seek support for the novel project.

Fry's first prospect was the Office of Naval Research, an agency which, since the war, had pursued a promisingly open-minded policy of support for university research projects. His proposal to the biophysics branch of the Office of Naval Research met with surprising success: he was granted $50,000 for the next year's research. The support surprised Fry because almost no one in the University except Everitt considered the project both serious and worthwhile. The skepticism was largely justifiable. Fry was new to the Department, the area of research he proposed to enter was new to the College, and the methods he chose were new to the world.

In September of 1948 the Bioacoustics Laboratory was formed, with William Fry as director. The Laboratory's small staff faced immediate problems: they needed equipment, some of which would have to be specially built; they needed supplies, including experimental animals; but most of all they needed room.

The Electrical Engineering Department was an unlikely place to find it. Virtually the whole Department was cramped into a small, antiquated building which had been added to and rearranged in every direction as far as possible—and it was full. Fry had been assigned a small office, but was told that there was simply no laboratory space available, and that he would be notified as soon as anything opened up.

He did not intend to wait. Deciding that a functioning laboratory was more important than office space, he immediately installed equipment in his cubicle and looked elsewhere for a place to park his desk. He finally found an unoccupied spot in a steam tunnel under the building. The tunnel was so low that it was necessary to crouch to enter his "office," and it was impossible to stand upright at his desk. As summer came on, the unventilated, pipe-filled tunnel began to resemble a turkish bath in a catacomb. And beneath everything was a layer of water that rose from the floor drains with every heavy rain. Fry acquired a kind of notoriety.

In order to make room for his laboratory equipment, Fry moved his desk out of his office into the only available space—a steam tunnel beneath the Electrical Engineering Research Laboratory.

The growing animal colony of the new Laboratory was hardly a secret to the other researchers in the building. Their complaints to Fry and to Everitt grew in frequency and volume until a climactic period in 1949, when the Department's candy vending machine began delivering mouse-scarred candy bars. There were bitter rumors that the culprits were escapees from the Bioacoustics Laboratory cages. Only when the mice—wild ones—were caught did the grumbling stop.

Animal problems of another sort faced Everitt, now Dean of the College of Engineering, when he returned from a trip to face two matrons who confronted him with a newspaper advertisement which read, "Wanted: Healthy cats. Will pay $2.00 for animals to be used in biological experiment. Call 2283." The ladies, cat fanciers both, accused Everitt of encouraging catnapping and hinted that he and his colleagues were something less than human. The astonished Everitt assured them that he knew nothing of the ad, that his family loved their own pet cats, and that he would set matters right immediately. When he checked with Fry he learned that the Bioacoustics Laboratory had found problems with their regular source of experimental animals, but that the advertisement was the handiwork of a graduate student whose zeal exceeded his knowledge of public relations. Everitt withdrew the advertisement and thought the problem solved, only to be called a week later by one of the ladies, who challenged, "I've been thinking, Dr. Everitt. If you're as interested in pets as you seem to be, you really should belong to the Humane Society. Are you a member? I'm treasurer of the local chapter."

Everitt was trapped. "It cost me $25 to save myself and Fry, and I couldn't even charge the cost to the College. But I certainly proved to the world that I love cats."

To some, Fry himself looked like as much of a nuisance as his animals. In his quest for laboratory space his methods can kindly be called unorthodox. Sometimes Bill and Frank, after a surveillance of some apparently unusable cranny in the building, would obtain official but seemingly pointless permission to use the space, quietly alter the niche to suit their purposes (usually, as it happened, at night) and set up shop in their new do-it-themselves annex. There were many strong after-the-fact objections by physical plant employees who thought the Fry brothers were infringing on their trades.

Everitt found himself in the crossfire. He usually managed to pacify the offended parties and, predictably, Fry usually remained as the room's tenant.

Everitt's role as administrative champion for the unruly Fry and the Laboratory might have ended early but for the progress the research produced. The Bioacoustics Laboratory had, by fair means or foul, managed to acquire the space and assemble the equipment for a serious research effort.

From the first the results were promising. With specially built, high-energy ultrasonic irradiating equipment, Fry began to study the effects of sound energy on different kinds of animal tissue. Four critical points were discovered: first, that ultrasound *did* affect all the kinds of tissue tested; second, that its effects could be made either temporary or permanent, depending on how much sound energy was applied; third, that different tissue components were affected by different amounts of radiation; and last, that repeated exposures to ultrasound below the threshold level of permanent damage would not injure the irradiated tissues.

A feline subject of an experiment is taken to the recovery room after ultrasonic irradiation.

To Fry, these facts pointed to a whole new technique for exploring the brain. Luckily, the tissue which seemed most susceptible to ultrasound was the threadlike, interconnecting, impulse-carrying components of the nerve cells. Slightly more resistant were the main nerve cell bodies, and still more tolerant to ultrasound were the supporting cells. Blood vessels were least affected.

Fry saw a way to use these variations to selectively alter brain tissues so that the organization of the cells could be analyzed, but he knew that two obstacles would have to be overcome. In the first place, his ultrasound equipment must be able to pinpoint its energy to the tiny areas occupied by critical nerve groups. And, second, the researchers would have to locate these small areas within the brains of living animals without surgically exploring for them, since the surgery would irreparably damage the very tissues they wanted to study.

The first problem was a technical one, one in which Frank Fry was to play a valuable part. The design of a carefully calibrated, high-powered sound generator incorporated a disc of quartz set into vibration by an oscillating electrical signal at frequencies 50 times too high to be heard by the human ear. A special lens in front of the disc focused the sound energy to a tiny point capable of stunning or destroying living tissues.

The second difficulty was anatomical: the animal under irradiation had to be held perfectly still, with its head position located to within hundredths of an inch, relative to the ultrasonic beam. The Bioacoustics Laboratory staff adapted previous techniques and developed new, more precise ones for finding brain "landmarks" with X rays, and used special head holders to position the anesthetized animals.

To study the path of a nerve chain, they would ultrasonically destroy one link, wait for the degeneration of the rest of the chain to occur, sacrifice the animal, then microscopically trace the path of degenerated nerve cells through the brain. Ultrasound, however, unlike the surgical, chemical, and electrical methods ordinarily used to disable nerve cells, inflicted no injury on tissue between the brain surface and the area to be destroyed. Nor did it indiscriminately destroy valuable tissues such as blood vessels near or within the lesion, as did these other methods. In addition, large, odd-shaped lesions could be produced by multiple irradiations, and areas tinier than the exposed lead of a pencil could be knocked out precisely and completely.

Temporary changes could be produced with smaller doses of radiation, and tests made of the changes in the experimental animal's physical abilities and in the behavior of its brain. After the effects of irradiation disappeared the same brain area or a different one could be affected again and the tests repeated. Thus a powerful new technique might be applied to exploring the functions and interrelations of brain regions.

The biggest disadvantage of the system was that the

Four ultrasonic generators are aimed by Fry so that their beams are focused at a single point.

ultrasonic beam required a bone-free path, since bone deflected the sound beam and absorbed so much of the energy that it was heated to the point of injuring nearby tissues. This meant that a window must be cut into the skull of the irradiated subject—an operation more serious-sounding than serious.

With the unique abilities made possible by the new technique, Fry and his growing laboratory staff embarked on the giant task of mapping the brain circuits in detail. Following the interdisciplinary approach he had seen used so successfully during the war, Fry acquired for the Bioacoustics Laboratory experts in neuroanatomy and neurophysiology, as well as additional staff members from the physical sciences.

But this expansion took money, both for new salaries and for expensive instrumentation. The liberal, easily won support of ONR's biophysics branch had shrunk abruptly after the first year. Fry turned to the physics branch of the agency. His proposal was received and read with interest by Elizabeth Kelly, a research coordinator for the agency and a physicist in her own right. Some of her superiors, however, reacted to the idea in a way that plagued Fry's efforts for years: they were skeptical that his approach would be a fruitful one, and they doubted that he or any other physical scientist could solve what was basically a biological problem. Their answer, though polite, was negative.

Fry sent feelers out to a half dozen other possible sponsors in fields ranging from engineering to medicine, but they all found reasons to withhold their support. Biological agencies, besides having doubts about this physicist's competence in their realm, were alarmed at the equipment costs he estimated. Funding agencies for physics and engineering research questioned the capability of this nonconformist who found it necessary to wander so far from traditional lines of study.

Fry considered his position, regrouped, and attacked again. His next proposal to ONR stressed that he wanted to develop ultrasonic transducers—the sources of high-frequency sound—and almost incidentally mentioned their application to a study of the nervous system. This proposal went through.

The situation eased somewhat when Elizabeth Kelly, who had performed biophysics research herself, became the new head of the biophysics section of ONR. From that post she supported the work of the Bioacoustics Laboratory until, in September, 1954, she left to join the Laboratory staff herself. Within a year she and Bill Fry were married.

Without formal training in the field, Fry had set out to become a neuroanatomist. In time the formidable geography and nomenclature of the central nervous system were as familiar to him as the abstruse analytical elements of ultrasonics. During the next seven years, as Fry and his unique laboratory established reputations for themselves, reports of research in the Bioacoustics Laboratory began to appear in journals of neuroanatomy, electrical engineering, acoustics, and other fields.

Everitt still found himself Fry's chief administrative benefactor, although the Electrical Engineering Department as a whole had come to appreciate Fry's peculiar talents. After a two-year struggle, Fry moved the Laboratory into a more adequate building. The name of the Laboratory was changed to the Biophysical Research Laboratory. Things began to look a bit brighter.

In 1955 Fry received a call from Russell Meyers, a surgeon at the State University of Iowa Hospitals in Iowa City. Meyers had read of the Biophysical Research Laboratory's work and was intrigued by the prospects of human brain surgery with ultrasound. Fry was pleased: here was an offer of support from one of the most highly regarded neurosurgeons in the country, a man with the competence to help actively in their research.

Fry accepted Meyers' offer, arranging to commute to Iowa City for tests of ultrasound's ability to help human patients. Meyers made the administrative arrangements and Bill and Frank Fry designed the irradiating machinery and operating area. The equipment was modeled after that at the Biophysical Research Laboratory, but included improvements dictated by the earlier experiments.

The completed irradiator and equipment for holding a precise location in the human brain were installed at Iowa City, and on March 21, 1958, the first operation was performed.

The patient, a victim of Parkinson's disease, was selected because his tremors and stiffness had not responded well to other treatments. Conventional surgical procedures had shown, however, that the destruction of certain small volumes of brain tissue might block the abnormal nerve impulses which produced his symptoms.

Before the operation Fry was uneasy. He and his associates had spent seven years testing and proving the technique on animals before he even discussed the possibility of applying it to humans; he and Meyers had studied the case from every angle; they would take every possible precaution; yet the thought haunted him that all the calculations of direction, strength, and duration of the ultrasonic beam were his, and that a mistake might cost the patient his eyesight, his reason, or his life. Fry was not a physician, and he lacked the physician's professional familiarity with matters of life and death.

The procedure took 12 hours and was a mild success. It had been planned and executed as a safe, conservative test of the ultrasonic technique, and it had brought about some improvement in the patient's condition. Most important, the irradiation itself had not seemed to harm the patient. Fry, Meyers, and their colleagues were encouraged.

The next patient, another victim of Parkinson's disease, was a more dramatic success. His symptoms disappeared almost completely after irradiation, and he suffered no noticeable side effects. The experiments continued, with the staffs of the Laboratory and the Iowa City Hospital gaining

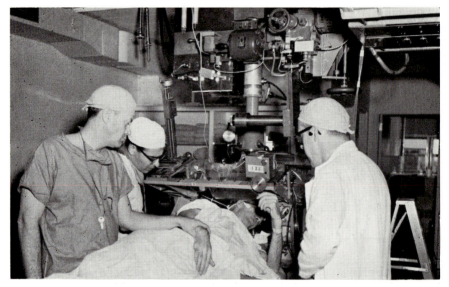

In 1958 a series of ultrasound treatments on human patients was begun. Eventually 88 patients with a variety of disorders were irradiated.

confidence and ability with each trial. A variety of afflictions were treated, including Parkinson's disease, cerebral palsy, the aftereffects of stroke, and "phantom" images and pain following amputation.

One of the most startling experiments involved an amputee. Polio, contracted as a child, eventually required that his right leg be amputated in a series of operations years apart which took first his foot, then his knee, and finally his thigh (which had borne a tormenting ulcer) to the hip. He continued to experience some sensations like those from the intact limb, especially severe pain from several parts of the "phantom" leg and foot.

Meyers and Fry planned to eliminate these symptoms by ultrasonically severing nerve fibers in the patient's brain. A tape recording made during the operation conveys the drama of the experiment and its unexpected result. These are excerpts from a conversation that lasted for five hours:

Meyers: Now in just a minute or two you will hear me count down from nine to zero—then the sound will go through. It will be too high-pitched for you to hear. You might feel some warm sensation—you might feel some dizziness—I want you to tell me what you feel in any case. The sound won't take any longer than three seconds for any one "buzz"—we may have to "buzz" you from ten to 20 times depending on our results. Then I will test you in between. I'll be here and you can raise any questions you want. We will work together here, the whole team, to get rid of this phantom and the pain that goes with it. . . . We have one minute to go. . . . 15 seconds now. . . . Did you feel anything?

Patient: A warm sensation.

Meyers: Warm sensation? Where was the warm sensation—all through your head or just a part?

Patient: Part.

Meyers: Still there?

Patient: No.

Meyers: Just passed off very quickly? OK. That's fine. Anything you notice about the phantom or the pain in the phantom—for that matter, anything—I want you to feel free to tell us. We are very eager to know of any experience you get. . . . Now, two minutes, going on three minutes. Now do you notice any changes in your phantom at all?

Patient: No, sir.

Meyers begins the neurological examination. The patient interrupts during the regular questions and answers, but his remarks are unclear:

Meyers: You what? . . . You mean your phantom foot, you mean it's straightened out, from what to what? You mean that, instead of feeling more folded up on itself, it feels less folded but not completely straight? Is that the only change in the phantom that you experience?

Patient: Yes.

Meyers: The patient indicates that the phantom foot on the right, which ordinarily feels almost like a fist, now feels straightened out to some degree. Now, can you estimate to what degree?

Patient: About 80 per cent straightened out.

A sensory examination indicates no change, and preparation is made for another ultrasound shot:

Fry: About one minute to go. . . . 30 seconds.

Meyers: Get ready. . . . Now. Did you get any experience at all that time?

Patient: Warm sensation.

The questioning stops, but a few moments later the conversation of Meyers and Fry is interrupted by the patient:

Patient: Image of the foot is gone.

Meyers: You mean you don't "see" the image there any more?

Patient: No.

Meyers: But you have the leg and the thigh?

Patient: Yes.

Meyers: When did you first notice this?

Patient: Just when I told you.

Meyers: Just when you told me. Did it seem to disappear suddenly or go away gradually like a moving picture fading away?

Patient: Gradually faded away.

After the neurological examination, preparations are made for the third ultrasound shot:

Meyers: After 38 minutes the patient states that he is still free of his phantom and phantom discomfort. Fifteen seconds. . . . Now. Did you get a warm sensation that time?

Patient: Yes.

Meyers: And did the warm sensation extend into your limb?

Patient: No.

Meyers: Not to your phantom at all. All right. You are not nauseated. Good. Now, do you still image what is left of your phantom? In other words, you image everything from about halfway between your knee and your ankle, right? On up to your trunk?

Patient: Yes, sir.

Again the patient is examined. The fourth ultrasound shot elicits no change, and preparation is made for the fifth shot:

Meyers: Twenty seconds. Get ready. . . . What did you experience that time?

Patient: Same warmth.

Meyers: Same warmth all through the head?

Patient: Yes.

Meyers: Nowhere else?

Patient: The ulcer has gone away.

Fry: Did he just recognize that? How soon?

Meyers: That would be estimated at about 20 seconds. . . . Now that the ulcer has gone, has there been any change in the phantom itself? How's that? The rest of the leg is gone? The whole leg?

Patient: Up to the hip.

Meyers: There goes the rest of the phantom. That was within ten seconds. Less than ten seconds—nine seconds—he says there goes the rest of it. That was within nine seconds from the beginning of the irradiation, not the end of it. . . . Now envision the bottom of your trunk—is it like it was healed following the last operation? Is that correct?

Patient: Yes, sir.

Meyers: Without any of the ulceration or the soreness of the ulceration, and without any of the pain?

Patient: That's right.

Meyers: Did that disappear fast or slow?

Patient: It went fast.

The remarkable elimination of the phantom limb, in the same stages as its physical departure, was never duplicated. Previous phantom limb cases had been treated by interrupting other brain structures, but none of their successes were as dramatic as this one.

Toward the end of the series—there were 88 cases in all, over a period of four years—several improvements were either tried or discussed. The single marathon operation of removing a bone flap in the patient's skull, irradiating him, and closing the opening was split into several parts. First the bone flap was removed, a small piece of plastic film was inserted to keep the skull opening clear, and the scalp was closed over the skull opening. Then any number of sessions of irradiation through the skin could take place over a period of time, with only the minor surgery required to place the patient in the head holder necessary at each session. When the total irradiation had been performed the bone flap could be replaced and the scalp closed for the final time.

Fry also devised a rigid ultrasound-transparent "window" which could be installed temporarily in place of the bone flap, performing the protective function of that part of the skull while allowing ultrasound to pass through unhindered.

The progress and results of the experiments were reported in medical journals and meetings, and the new knowledge gained by Fry and Meyers helped to broaden the clinical work of neurosurgeons across the country. In a paper entitled "Fifty Years of Neurosurgery" in the *International Abstracts of Surgery*, Dr. John E. Scarff made the following comment about the ultrasonic technique:

Ultrasonic surgery would appear to represent the ultimate in surgery. It goes one step beyond stereotaxic surgery in refinement in that it permits the precise placement of discrete lesions at chosen points within the depth of the brain without leaving even the track of a needle or electrode in the intervening tissue. It undoubtedly will open up, even more widely than at present, new fields for physiologic research.

By the late 1950's Fry felt that he had proved his point at Iowa City, and that the work there had cost heavily in terms of progress in the brain mapping project, which was central to his interest. Financial support for the Laboratory, while substantial, had not met Fry's hopes. As the cooperative program at Iowa City progressed he and his colleagues at Urbana had seen ways to improve their equipment and techniques enough to ready them for clinical use. Fry thought his results justified the improvements, but in saying so he made some predictions which made prospective sponsors think twice:

> Although some of the results already achieved are rather exciting when compared with past capabilities, it is apparent that the field is in a primitive state compared to the future potential . . . its rate of attainment is determined to a major extent by the economic status of the field as determined by agencies which provide the financial support. . . . A support level at least two orders of magnitude [one hundred times] greater than that currently available to the field will be necessary. . . .

There was debate in medical circles over the significance of the Iowa City studies, and Fry's University support was lagging to some extent because of his own policies: strings were tightened on Illinois' aid to Fry because he consistently failed to involve sufficient numbers of graduate students in the Biophysical Research Laboratory's work, thereby violating one of the tenets of the University's research policy—that research was to benefit and be benefited by education.

Possible sponsors in the medical fields were approached: many were interested, but none had the combination of funds and pioneering policy that would enable them to assume the burden of an entirely new line of research. Critics caught Fry in a pincers argument—his philosophy of using ultrasound on a large variety of cases, they felt, limited the number of successes of any single kind to too small a number to be statistically convincing.

Fry made a virtue of necessity. Since the human studies could not be expanded to the degree he felt was appropriate, and since a really searching study of brain organization seemed even more clearly overdue, he chose to take the obvious course. Quietly and rather suddenly the human irradiations ended in 1959. The Biophysical Research Laboratory resumed its efforts to map the brain. The study could now benefit from new tools, new researchers, and new experience.

The plan, still under way, is not novel as far as new ultrasonic procedures are concerned, and it is not fast. It *is* astounding. A small nerve structure of the cat brain has

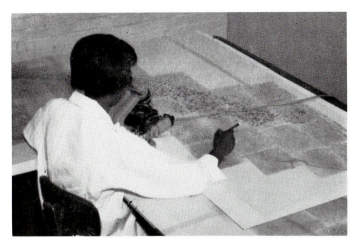

Graduate students in the Biophysical Research Laboratory assist in the preparation of detailed maps of cat brain circuits. Critical nerve cells have been
differentiated by ultrasonic irradiation.

been selected as the first target. Tiny lesions are placed at
selected points, the animals are kept alive for periods long
enough to allow nerve tissues associated with those of the
lesions to degenerate, then the animals are sacrificed and
their brains carefully stained and mounted on thousands of
microscope slides. Then a painstaking microscope search
compares irradiated nerve structures with their undamaged
counterparts or other reference structures, revealing by
comparison the cells missing in the tissue under examination. Since the absent cells are those linked functionally to
the regions irradiated, their positions can be located in the
normal tissue. Finally, huge maps are drawn of the region,
cell by cell. From these maps circuit diagrams like those
used in electronics will be drawn—the first quantitative
information about brain structure hookups ever gathered.

The price of this precision is high: 30 full-time staff
members of the Laboratory worked three and a half years
to provide enough data for Fry to analyze in order to derive
the circuitry of brain structures less than one-tenth the size
of a pea. A comparable analysis of the entire human brain
would take thousands of times longer.

The implications of the work are staggering. A completely new kind of knowledge of the brain and its work-
ings has become possible—the brain might understand itself. Surgical treatment of brain disorders might be su-
perseded by safer, more specific therapy. Physical changes

related to emotional phenomena could be traced, and ways to exploit the brain's vast potentialities might be discovered. Designers of computers and other sophisticated electronic devices might find clues in the circuitry of the brain for building improved machines with such spectacular abilities as self-awareness and self-repair.

But after the brain mapping began, financial support for the Laboratory seemed, if anything, less dependable than ever. A non-University sponsor supplying almost half the Biophysical Research Laboratory's funds indicated its intention not to renew its support unless the Laboratory added a formally trained, professional neuroanatomist to its staff. University officials stated that unless the Biophysical Research Laboratory expanded the involvement of graduate students, the University could not increase its support to pay the salary of the new man.

Fry was worried. His laboratory, unique in the world, might have to close. Loss of half his support would almost halt the already plodding pace of the brain mapping research. Fry agreed to involve more graduate students in the study, which was already taking an average of 12 hours a day of his own time. Soon afterward the University officials approved the extra funds, and the support for the Laboratory was assured.

But more than 15 years of hard work to establish the Laboratory took its toll on Bill Fry: he suffered a serious heart attack. Months passed before Fry could return to his work. Meanwhile his brother, whose activities had expanded over the years to include surgery and biological studies, took over the post of acting director of the Laboratory. Bill's wife and the other members of the now-sizable staff continued working. When Fry returned in 1965 he was full of new plans—plans which could be met now that this latest financial crisis had passed.

Many of these plans are now being implemented. One change will be toward automation: computers will be linked to the X-ray machines, head holders, and irradiating machine so that the process of irradiation can be freed from human slowness and error. A project in the Department of Computer Science to develop a pattern recognition computer, ILLIAC III, may lend machine assistance to the painstaking job of identifying cells of irradiated brain tissues.

With even more complex instrumentation, the mapping

might take a much faster course. By linking a computer-controlled ultrasonic beam to another computer analyzing the effects of that beam on the brain, it might be possible to literally track nerve paths through the brain automatically. Ideas still undeveloped point the way for completely eliminating the element of surgery from ultrasonic irradiation—perhaps reducing intricate and dangerous brain surgery to safe office or clinical procedures.

The cost of such instruments, of course, would be tremendous—comparable to that of the equipment used to control missiles and space ships at Cape Kennedy. But physicist Fry defends the expense: "The study and correction of malfunctions of the human brain—the most complex mechanism yet identified by man—would appear to warrant the development and use of instrumentation which is at least comparable in sophistication to that currently in use in investigations of the physical world."

His point seems valid. And, despite the difficulty of his goal, Fry may have his way. He has already had considerable success in changing people's minds.

THE NONTHINKING MACHINES

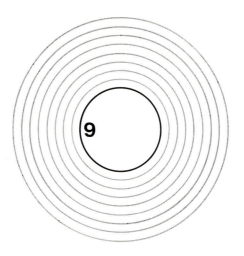

February 16, 1952, was a cold, overcast day on the University of Illinois campus. A wind that would not have been noticeable in milder weather carried an extra sting of dust. At the loading dock of the Electrical Engineering Research Laboratory a shivering driver in army fatigues tugged at the rear doors of an olive-drab trailer truck, found them secure, and hurried to the warmth of the truck cab. On its door was stenciled, "U.S. ARMY ORDNANCE CORPS." The few men behind the truck, some in suits and some in shirtsleeves, disappeared into the building. The truck pulled slowly away, and with it went one of the most complex, sophisticated machines in the world—the University of Illinois' only operating digital computer.

The University computer was one of the first of such machines, yet its basic features would remain common to computers for decades to come. Throughout its evolution the automatic digital computer has been composed of five basic units: a data input unit, a memory unit which retains information, an arithmetic unit where calculations are performed, a control unit which operates the computer according to instructions fed into the machine, and a data output unit. Like the familiar desk-top adding machine, the computer deals exclusively with numbers; adding, subtracting, multiplying, and dividing them. Unlike the desk calculator, the computer's operations must be specified in advance by a plan of written instructions called a program, which it follows automatically. The computer can also compare one number with another, selecting the larger or smaller one, and use the outcome of this test to guide subsequent operations.

The computer is not limited to numerical problems. Numbers can symbolize military units on a battlefield, shock waves on an aircraft wing, or countless other possibilities. Thus the computer is more than a super desk calculator; it is a powerful symbol-manipulator as well. But while it is a quick and methodical servant, the computer is completely helpless. Its repertoire of abilities is limited entirely by the men who design the machine and write its programs.

While a complete history of computers would probably have to begin with a cave man and his fingers, the modern era of automatic computation began in 1925 at the Massachusetts Institute of Technology, where researchers under the direction of Vannevar Bush assembled an analog calculator. In this machine the quantities being computed were represented by the angles of rotation of gears. This device and a secret descendant of it proved useful during World War II for computing tables of numbers by which artillery was aimed.

In 1939 work began on a machine which would automatically perform sequences of calculations without the intervention of a human operator. The computer, which became known as the Mark I, was the brain-child of Howard Aiken, a Harvard physicist, and was built with the support of the International Business Machines Corporation. Completed in 1944, the Mark I operated at Harvard for more than a decade and a half.

Before the Mark I was put into operation, however, plans had begun at the Moore School of Electrical Engineering of the University of Pennsylvania for a much more advanced machine. The ENIAC—Electronic Numerical Integrator And Calculator—was the first electronic computer, since it used vacuum tubes in place of the electromechanical relays and switches of earlier calculators. By the time it went into operation in 1946 it was also the most complicated electronic device in the world. Containing over 18,000 tubes, the computer was plagued by vast problems of cooling and maintenance.

Louis Ridenour, Dean of the Graduate College at the University of Illinois, followed the progress of automatic computing machines closely. He realized the importance of the new calculators and hoped that the University could become involved in computer technology. Others at the University held the same view, among them Electrical Engineering and Civil Engineering Department heads William L. Everitt and Nathan M. Newmark. Ridenour, Everitt, Newmark, and others in engineering, physics, and mathematics promoted the idea of Illinois' involvement with computers. In 1948 they succeeded. At its January meeting the Board of Trustees appropriated $150,000 for the purchase of a computer from the Reeves Instrument Company of New York.

A committee headed by Newmark was set up to deal with the new project. Two of its members would play long and decisive roles: Abraham Taub, a mathematician who had only recently joined the University staff; and Ralph Meagher, a physicist who had just received his Ph.D. at Illinois. The two men were little alike. Taub was authoritative and quick-tempered, while Meagher was unemotional and meticulous to the point of irritating those around him.

The agreement with the Reeves Instrument Company was a cautious one. The computer which Reeves proposed to build for Illinois, called the REEVAC, was based upon the optimistic hope that several difficult developmental steps could be made quickly, and the University contract for the purchase of the machine specified that Illinois could withdraw from the agreement if it appeared that Reeves could not meet the contract terms.

As it happened, the University's caution was justified. By June it became clear that the REEVAC was not progressing on schedule. John von Neumann, a pioneer in computer design at the Institute for Advanced Study in Princeton, New Jersey, wrote to Newmark, advising him that the Reeves work showed little promise. He suggested that Illinois, with its pool of talented men, build its own computer. At the same time Taub, fresh from an inspection tour of the Reeves project, made an equally dim prognosis of its success. He suggested that the University copy the computer von Neumann and his associates were planning at Princeton.

The authors of the Princeton project were asked whether Illinois might build a replica of the proposed von Neumann machine. On October 16, 1948, Robert Oppenheimer, Director of the Institute for Advanced Study at Princeton, wrote to Louis Ridenour:

We are only too glad to give you our encouragement to proceed. I believe that on the technical side we have already sent on the reports that were available and I think you may look forward to increasing collaboration.

By the end of the year the Reeves contract was canceled. The computer committee under Newmark pondered von Neumann's recommendations, added its own suggestions, and forwarded its findings to Dean Ridenour. In January of 1949 the Research Board, headed by Ridenour, sent its proposal to University President George Stoddard. The proposal recommended that the University build a copy of the von Neumann machine.

At this point the University's computer program got a valuable push from the Ballistic Research Laboratory at Aberdeen Proving Ground in Maryland. After preliminary talks with von Neumann and Ridenour, the Army Ordnance chiefs offered the following arrangement: If Illinois could build not one but *two* copies of the von Neumann machine, Aberdeen would buy the first at half the total cost. Since the proposition looked like a clear bargain for everyone, University officials gladly accepted.

Once the Army contract was signed, things moved rapidly. In February of 1949 a group, including some of the personnel from the earlier computer committee, was formally organized to build the computers. Ralph Meagher was named chief engineer for the project. The group's members set to work gathering information on the von Neumann machine (which was still under development), securing a site and personnel for the project, and considering possible changes from the original design.

By the time construction began in April, one departure from von Neumann's yet unsettled plan was firm. The Army computer, which had acquired the name of ORDVAC, would have a newly developed memory unit using cathode ray tubes—like miniature television picture tubes—to store information in the form of spots of electric charge (visible as fine points of green light) on the faces of the tubes. The promising but relatively untried system was known as the Williams electrostatic tube memory for its English inventor, F. C. Williams.

Soon a large part of the computer group's attention was directed toward developing this essential element of ORD-VAC. Because the storage spots on the tubes were so close to each other (1,024 locations on each five-inch round tube face), repeated signals at a single location would often "leak over" to an adjacent spot, causing an error.

Joseph Wier, one of the graduate assistants in the group, finally found an ingenious solution. His "twitch" system fired a burst of electrons just off-center from a nearly over-charged memory location; the resulting spatter of electrons redistributed the charge to a safe pattern. By May of 1950 Meagher was able to report to Dean Ridenour, "The University is perhaps one of ten organizations with models of electrostatic storage systems." Illinois, a newcomer to the field of automatic computation, was entering the front rank.

The ORDVAC project developed a special unity that bound the small research team together. Permeating every phase of the work was Ralph Meagher's painstaking crafts-manship. The number of checks and tests made was ex-traordinary, even for so precise a field as electronics. Be-tween the ORDVAC group at Illinois and von Neumann's group at Princeton there was constant correspondence, and soon it seemed possible that the copy might be completed before the original.

By the middle of 1951 the ORDVAC was beginning to show signs of life. Its memory unit was performing ade-quately, various arithmetic units had been built and checked, the control system seemed to function properly, and finally, in July, the ORDVAC ran its first programs. There were "bugs" in the system, but no major failures. The group was surprised and delighted: the care used to build the machine had paid dividends. The assembled computer was ten feet long, two feet wide, eight and one-half feet high, and weighed almost five tons. By September it was running smoothly.

As soon as it passed its initial tests, plans were made to ship the ORDVAC to Aberdeen. The trip itself would be the hardest test the computer would face: despite all the precautions taken to insure its safety, no piece of equipment as complex as the ORDVAC could be expected to suffer the

Ralph Meagher, the Illinois computer project's chief engineer, was the man most responsible for the reliability of the ORDVAC. This, the first computer constructed at the University, was built for the Aberdeen Proving Ground in Maryland.

750-mile trip to Maryland and then face the stringent reliability demands of computer operation without a major overhaul.

ORDVAC's builders began dismantling the machine on the morning of February 11, 1952, and by the sixteenth the computer was in an Army truck on its way to Aberdeen. It arrived three days later, and stood completely assembled on February 29. Within a week the ORDVAC was put into operation. Surprisingly, there were only a few broken connections and bad tubes. The Illinois computer crew which had come to set up the machine was elated, and immediately set about putting it through rigid acceptance tests.

The first week of March was a hectic one, but not without amusement. One day an Aberdeen colonel strode into the computer room, where the University researchers were up to their elbows in the innards of the ORDVAC, and asked for the man in charge. It was some time before he could be convinced that he wanted Meagher, who, forever tidy, was sweeping the floor.

The acceptance tests, designed to check every facet of the computer's reliability and power, might reasonably have

Thousands of tests and adjustments were necessary to set the ORDVAC in operation.

required months of calibration and adjustment. But just a week after it arrived, the University team left. The computer personnel at Aberdeen were amazed to learn that the computer had been checked so quickly. Familiarizing its new owners with the computer and completing contract negotiations took four months. Five months after its arrival the ORDVAC had made itself at home.

The Director of the Ballistic Research Laboratories, Colonel Alden Taber, wrote, "As far as we know, it is the first time in the history of the high-speed computing machines that one has been completed . . . within the period of the contract. . . . The Ballistic Research Laboratories cannot be too enthusiastic in their praise of this group."

Louis Ridenour, now head of his own California computer enterprise, wrote Ralph Meagher: "As you can imagine, I am most impressed by your great success in moving the ORDVAC to Aberdeen and getting it going again in its new location. This is a most convincing demonstration of the virtues of the machine and of the skill of its builders, but—as you know—I have been convinced on these scores for some time now."

The Illinois group had assembled a computer whose combination of speed and memory was unmatched in the world, and had done it so quickly that its appearance predated even that of von Neumann's own machine. From Meagher's meticulousness came the reliability, so critical under ordinary circumstances, which had survived the cross-country trip. And this was the group's first computer—although by now ORDVAC's stay-at-home twin was under construction.

But the University had not heard the last of ORDVAC. For up to eight hours each night problems were fed to the ORDVAC over a teletype circuit from Illinois, and minutes later the answers would appear there on tape. This long-distance consultation lasted until September, when the University had a computer of its own.

The new computer, the University's half of the Aberdeen-Illinois deal, was the first built and owned entirely by an educational institution. It soon acquired the title of ILLIAC and a reputation for reliability surpassing even that of the ORDVAC. One of the men chiefly responsible for the machine's reliability was James Robertson. An electrical engineer, Robertson was an expert in error-checking systems and a contributor to the design of the twin computers' arithmetic machinery.

Another ingredient in the ILLIAC's reliability was a system of thorough preventive maintenance, centering around a special "leapfrog" test devised by David Wheeler, an English mathematician who came to Illinois from Cambridge University. The leapfrog test enabled the ILLIAC to examine itself, checking sequentially each segment of the circuitry by imposing a number of heavy loads on it in quick succession. When a weak component showed up, the test localized the trouble to perhaps ten or fifteen tubes of 2,800 total.

But the ILLIAC was not an easy machine to use. A researcher with a problem to submit to the computer had to translate it into terms the ILLIAC could deal with in its own operations—rather like a patient needing to know medical Latin to visit the doctor. Now that the basic computer was working, the Illinois group could devote some time to making it more comfortable to live with. In charge of this part of the project was mathematician John P. Nash. A tall, affable Texan, Nash was a diplomat who thrived on the problems of supply, finance, and organization.

As the ILLIAC grew less formidable, the demand for computer time grew. Originally the machine had run 16 hours a day, four for warm-up and maintenance, and 12

ILLIAC I, almost identical to the ORDVAC, was the first computer built and owned entirely by an academic institution.

hours for solving problems. To meet the increased need, the computer's hours were extended to 24 hours a day, five days a week, and finally six days a week.

The ILLIAC's engineers found that they could best play the computer by ear. Throughout the building speakers were arranged which constantly broadcast the noises the computer produced as it ran. A halt in the pattern of beeps and whistles meant that either the ILLIAC had finished its problem, or something was wrong. One Christmas an enterprising engineer wrote a program from which the computer could play "Silent Night" for its weary-eared crew.

Life with the ILLIAC was never dull. Once an especially persistent malady struck the computer. Meagher and his colleagues searched and tested for over 60 hours to find the answer—and when they found it, their reaction was a mixture of anger and relief. The fault lay not with the ILLIAC but with the University's powerful betatron, whose operation was causing a drop in the voltage of the electric power ten times each second. The cure was administered at the betatron, and the ILLIAC never suffered a recurrence of the ailment again.

By the mid-1950's, however, ILLIAC was beginning to show its weaknesses. Improvements in transistors made their substitution for vacuum tubes a very attractive possibility for reducing both the size and heat problems of computers like the ILLIAC. Other advances seemed likely in areas of circuitry, logic, and parallel operation (formerly sequential operations could, it appeared, be telescoped so that they overlapped or occurred simultaneously).

In January of 1956 the computer group, now formalized as the Digital Computer Laboratory, presented its ideas to the Atomic Energy Commission in Washington. The Laboratory's choice of this possible sponsor was an obvious one: John von Neumann had become an AEC Commissioner, and the Commission had just begun its special mathematics and computer program under John Pasta, who would later head the Digital Computer Laboratory himself. In June, a one-hundred-thousand-dollar contract was granted to finance a thorough study of the DCL experts' ideas.

With this support the researchers set to work to discover how to build the fastest computer yet. By December of 1957 they had developed a plan. DCL Report Number 80, "On the Design of a Very High-Speed Computer," described the results of almost two years of study and experimentation, and pointed the way to a new generation of computers.

The keynote of the study was speed. A calculator incorporating its ideas would be 100 times as fast as the ILLIAC, ten times as fast as any other computer in existence, and at least twice as fast as any proposed computer. The machine so intrigued the AEC that they promised two million dollars to the project—one-half million per year for the next four years. Work on ILLIAC II began immediately.

Again development of the computer's memory was an important part of the project. The new ILLIAC was to have three memory sections of different sizes and speeds, to replace the Williams tube memory which had provided so many of ILLIAC I's growing pains. Fastest of these was a small unit whose information would be available in only two ten-millionths of a second.

This special memory section followed an odd course of development. Meagher assigned Wolfgang Poppelbaum, a transistor specialist, and Joseph Wier, whose "twitch" method had improved the old Williams tube memory, the same job: developing fast circuits for the computer. But Poppelbaum was to employ transistors, and Wier was to use tubes.

"He had set up a race," recalls Poppelbaum. "No one

Thousands of tiny magnetic iron rings strung on a mesh of wires compose one of the memory units of ILLIAC II.

called it that, but it was just the same. Not that we didn't cooperate—sometimes, in fact, Joe would work with transistors and I'd switch to tubes—but there was an extra stimulus of competition. I remember when we had to put some of the chassis in pans of water to cool them, because we were working them so hard."

By the time construction began on ILLIAC II, the "race" had a winner: the computer itself. Out of the time-cutting research had come valuable new ideas for transistorized fast computer memories. While these ideas were being turned into devices inside the new Digital Computer Laboratory building, the University purchased other, commercially built computers to meet the growing demands for computer availability.

In April of 1959 Ralph Meagher left the University to work as an independent consultant. He was replaced as director by Abraham Taub, one of the shrinking company of "old timers" in the still-young Digital Computer Laboratory.

A succession of increasingly complex test models of IL-LIAC II were built and expanded, some of which eventually became parts of the complete computer. During the summer of 1960 the heart of the new machine was gradually assembled. By August, 1962, the central high-speed portions were checked, and, with the addition of a small memory unit and minimal input and output equipment, ILLIAC II began its useful life. Its major acceptance test involved the solution of a complex problem in gas dynamics. Before its first problem was finished, the new computer had performed approximately half a billion arithmetic operations—an hour's work that would have taken an eight-hours-a-day, five-days-a-week human computer over four months, if he could stand such a pace.

But at the Digital Computer Laboratory there was little pause for self-congratulations. The machine was still far from done: it was more than a year later, in the summer of 1963, before the computer could be said to run at full capacity. It had acquired and lost a half-dozen personalities in the meantime, for ILLIAC II was the center of an unending series of experiments in new programming systems and combined equipment operations. From IBM came a full assortment of peripheral equipment for the computer. And to develop its usefulness and versatility the researchers at Illinois invented improved schemes for using the machine.

The demand for ILLIAC II's services grew steadily as the overload mounted from the Laboratory's commercial service computer. Clearly its time should be used as profitably as possible—a scheduling problem so difficult that it was worthy of computer attention itself. As a result, early in its operations ILLIAC II was set up to operate in a "time-sharing" mode to deal with many problems at once, by constantly applying itself to the most immediate element of each task, and ignoring (although not noticeably) other problems for the time being.

A possibility pioneered at MIT and tested at Illinois applied this time-sharing principle to remote consoles connected to ILLIAC II via standard telephone connections. Under this arrangement a user might dial the number of ILLIAC II from a small unit, type in his problem or submit it from punched cards, punched tape, or magnetic tape, and without noticeable delay receive his answer over the same telephone cable.

An indication of the computer's reputation appeared in *Computing Reviews:* ". . . ILLIAC II, at its conception in the mid-1950's, represented, together with some other independent design projects of the same period, the spearhead and breakthrough into a new generation of machines."

ILLIAC II, a "second-generation" computer, was much larger and more complex than its University-built predecessors.

An even newer generation of computers is represented by the yet-unfinished ILLIAC III, a highly sophisticated general-purpose machine designed not only to do arithmetic, but also to recognize patterns in pictures.

In 1957, while engineers at Illinois were searching for ways to design machines with greater speed, researchers at the Lawrence Radiation Laboratory in Berkeley, California, were plagued with problems because a device they had built seemed to be too fast.

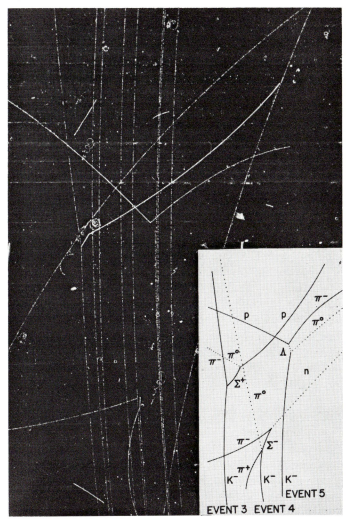

The problem of interpreting millions of bubble-chamber photographs such as this one triggered the development of ILLIAC III.

The troublemaker was not a computer but a giant new bubble chamber, an instrument which permitted scientists to photograph the tracks of subatomic particles and gather facts about the particles and their interactions. The machine got its name from the fact that it was filled with ultracold liquid hydrogen, which is so unstable that even invisible and almost massless elementary particles leave tiny vapor trails of bubbles through it.

The chamber was run around the clock, producing photographs of particle events every six seconds of the day or night. It was gathering data about the basic components of matter at a rate far too fast for the rest of the operation of "reading" the information on the pictures.

The problem was not unforeseen. Researchers at Berkeley had tried to minimize the time and human effort involved by relegating some of the simpler tasks to electronic computers. Among the men at Berkeley was a physicist, Bruce McCormick, who found his interest shifting from the particle-centered to the computer-centered side of the problem. By 1960 McCormick decided that his real interest lay in the broader field of computer recognition of patterns in general. He left to join the University of Illinois Digital Computer Laboratory.

Soon after he arrived, things began to happen. A proposal to the Atomic Energy Commission, dated December 1, 1960, sought backing "For a Study of the Pattern Recognition and Data Handling Problems Arising in the Analysis of Bubble Chamber Photographs of High Energy Particle Events." McCormick believed that a computer system adequate to handle bubble chamber photographs would also be suited to a wider range of applications.

The Atomic Energy Commission was interested in the project. With its support, early in 1961 McCormick headed a small group seeking ways to electronically decipher the information in bubble chamber films. Within a year the group had assembled photographic equipment able to view films one frame at a time and either scan or measure their contents. The two jobs were differentiated, since for such purposes as recognizing letters and words an ability to endure distortion of the image was important, while analysis of bubble chamber tracks required careful measurements.

By 1963 the circuitry had been developed for a preprocessor which would extract basic facts about the tracks on the pictures. This device would examine each picture piece by piece and note the origins, ends, and intersections of tracks within each section, and "retouch" the picture by clarifying the lines within it.

But because this unit treated the negative in sections, it would have to "think small." To remedy the mistakes resulting from this nearsightedness, other devices would reestablish the longer-range order of the idealized images. The tracks thus pinpointed would be analyzed by arithmetic units like those in conventional computers. Finally, the results of the whole process would be stored and presented by output equipment.

But by 1963 most of these units were still only ideas. The unusual parts of the system were to be built within the Digital Computer Laboratory, and the remainder subcontracted to commercial concerns. The task of awarding contracts, purchasing, and building were under way. McCormick recalls, "It was business as usual: terrible. One headache after another."

Meanwhile McCormick and a visiting Indian professor, Rangaswamy Narasimhan, had evolved a novel "linguistic approach" to pattern recognition which promised to ease the task of programming the pattern recognition computer. The experiments with the linguistic approach hinted at the usefulness of the system for analyzing aerial reconnaissance photographs, photos of cloud formations taken by weather satellites, and other information-laden pictures. How broad this class of applications might eventually be, McCormick could only guess:

There seem to be four immediate areas where a machine like ILLIAC III would be useful. First, in bubble chamber photo processing—where we started. Second, it would be useful for biological image processing like that of Bill Fry in Biophysics. Reading brain tissue slides would be a long but possible jump from bubble chamber work.

A third use would be in what I'd call a "Hospital Information Center." A machine like ILLIAC III would be the center of the operation, helping in diagnosing diseases, correlating lab tests (processing images in pathology and radiology, for example), handling patients' medical histories, and keeping financial records.

Fourth, an outgrowth of the project might make possible a kind of superlibrary: a "learning resource center." Books, experiments, discoveries—they could all be fed into the computer and automatically sorted, cataloged, and stored. We're building a device to store ten million visual images under computer-controlled selection. With tools like this we hope to create the sort of environment where a person could saturate his ability to learn.

But the ILLIAC story does not end here. An ILLIAC IV is in the works, still bigger and faster, and again it pioneers in new design ideas. The main concept in the machine is that of linking a single control unit with several hundred subunits, each of which has its own arithmetic and data storage abilities. The number of these subunits might be increased almost without limit.

The picture of Abraham Lincoln at left has been crudely digitized by a computer's scanning unit, which classifies the gradation of grays in the original into four tones. The second picture is a "cartoon" of the previous portrait, simplified by the computer, which decides whether any point in the picture should be black or white on the basis of the shades of its neighboring points.

The parallel construction of this system allows it to perform many, many operations simultaneously, like ingesting data and instructions in one gulp, rather than in the usual computer's more serial fashion, and performing calculations simultaneously whenever possible. For certain of these preliminary steps the subunits can act almost independently of each other, but whenever necessary they can be meshed to function like a single large computer.

The goal of this plan is speed. Like ILLIAC II, the new machine will leap ahead of its contemporaries in this aspect of performance, calculating 50 times as fast as any other computer now contemplated. More than a billion computations per second will be possible. Its builders have calculated, in fact, that ILLIAC IV will have a computing ability equal to the combined abilities of all the rest of the computers in the world.

With this speed the new computer will be able to handle tasks previously considered impossible. In weather forecasting, for example, accurate prognoses through the use of computers can be made, but with computers of today's speed a good 48-hour forecast requires 52 hours of computer time. ILLIAC IV will do the job in less than three hours. In the field of defense, radar can provide more accurate data about approaching missiles than present computers can handle in time to stop them, but ILLIAC IV will be able to locate them faster and more precisely. Nerve network studies of the brain will be simulated in greater complexity with the new machine than with previous computers. And the masses of data gathered by the University and other radio telescopes can be analyzed much more adequately with the complex mathematics of which IL-LIAC IV will be capable.

The total cost of the program has been estimated at more than eighteen million dollars. The design of ILLIAC IV will involve a joint effort of the University, other potential users, and industry. Indicative of the changing times, all of the components will be built by commercial manufacturers.

But if the business of designing, building, supervising, and using computers seems to have grown glamorous, and if the men involved look like more than ordinary mortals, they themselves won't hesitate to correct the impression. The man in charge of ILLIAC IV provides a good example.

Daniel Slotnick, a newcomer to the newly renamed Department of Computer Science, arrived in 1965 after working under John von Neumann at the Institute for Advanced Study and holding positions with IBM and Westinghouse. Although he is a young man, his reputation is international. He has a dry, sharp-edged wit, and is both perceptive and frank. And ILLIAC IV is, in his own words, "driving me nuts."

Construction of the computer has scarcely begun. Gone, however, are the idyllic days of ILLIAC I, when a small team of intellectual adventurer-handymen could face problems squarely, perhaps take chances, and feel that within limits their fates and that of the computer were in their hands. Now, as Slotnick explains ruefully, "I feel like an administrator. I'm dealing with a hundred damned companies, holding onto the purse strings, trying to assemble a crew for the project, haggling, hiring, firing—it's a mess."

And of course some days are worse than others. On one of the former an interviewer caught up to the harassed Slotnick and, in a moment of unobservant naïveté, asked about the state of the project. Replied the professor, with an obvious effort at self-control, "The project? . . . what would you like to know? Its history? Its present? Its future?" There was a pause. "If you want to report something, report this: We haven't changed the design in over two days now, and we're growing confident."

A STAR IN A BOTTLE

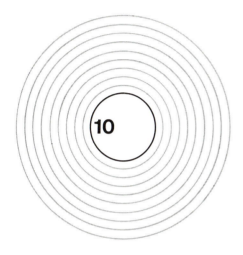

"If a sub didn't have to use electric motors to run submerged, it wouldn't have to come up to recharge the batteries. I can't see why a submarine couldn't stay under for months at a time," the young naval officer said.

"We'd still need oxygen for the crew," his companion reflected.

"But that's no problem. A sub could carry enough compressed air to supply the men for months. There would be some limitation, certainly, but air for the crew or for power wouldn't be a factor any more."

This conversation in the Naval Electronics Laboratories in San Diego, California, was typical of discussions being held by Navy men in the early 1950's. They were excited by the prospects of the atomic-powered submarine, which was as radical a departure from the conventional submarine as the submarine had been from the surface ship. An atomic engine could power a submarine for years without a breath of air.

Three men were present at the discussion. One of them, a civilian on leave from the University of Illinois, said very little. A tall, quiet man, Arnold Nordsieck was a physicist from the Control Systems Laboratory, better known on the campus as CSL, a laboratory created during the Korean War to perform classified research for the armed forces.

The conversation between the Navy men had raised an exciting idea in Nordsieck's mind. If the need for surfacing to recharge batteries no longer limited the submarine's capacity to stay submerged, surely its navigating capability would. He realized that navigational aids far more precise than the motor-driven gyroscopes of the day would be required. The accuracy of such gyros was limited by the friction and wear of the ball bearings that supported the rotors. The cumulative error this friction caused soon forced the submarine to surface in order to recalibrate its gyro with the stars. Nordsieck wondered if it might be possible to support a rotor with magnetic fields to free it from the friction of mechanical bearings.

The gyroscope he envisioned would work in principle exactly like a conventional gyro. It would maintain a reference direction by using the angular momentum of a rapidly spinning mass, the rotor. The axis of rotation would continue to point at a fixed spot in the sky (such as the North Star) regardless of any movement of its supporting frame, even inside a moving submarine. The only real difference between the electromagnetic gyro and an ordinary gyro would be in the means of supporting the rotor.

In the fall of 1956 Nordsieck returned to the University. The following spring he met with a group of CSL engineers and scientists to discuss the possibility of building the "electric vacuum gyroscope." They agreed that the difficulties involved would be formidable. They were aware of unsuccessful attempts to build similar gyros at other places in the past. They understood that the project would require specialized talents, extremely unusual materials, and the most sophisticated laboratory and manufacturing techniques known, as well as some yet to be developed. But Nordsieck had a powerful argument: "Since the armistice, people in the University have been embarrassed to have a military lab like ours on the campus. The gyro project can bring us into more fundamental areas of study and help show those people the value of having an interdisciplinary engineering lab.

"This project is tailor-made for us. It's the kind of work we want to get into, and I believe that if it can be built anywhere, it can be built here."

The main reasons for his confidence were seated on either side of him at the conference table. One was Daniel Alpert, a respected authority on ultrahigh vacuums, and the other was Howard Knoebel, an engineer who thrived on nearly impossible problems.

The gray-haired, crew-cut Alpert was CSL's technical director. A physicist who earned his Ph.D. at Stanford during World War II, he had come to Illinois from the Westinghouse Electric Corporation.

Howard Knoebel was a short, balding man who had a reputation for becoming expert in almost everything he tried—and he had tried almost everything. In addition to being an electronic systems designer, he was known to be an electrician, plumber, machinist, inventor, woodworker, musician, and automobile mechanic. These diverse interests and the consuming curiosity that drove him had detoured him from graduate study—he was simply too busy to finish graduate work. In many respects Nordsieck and Knoebel, the project leaders, were much alike. Both were intensely curious, good at working with their hands, and highly inventive.

The project team was never to become extremely large, but it attracted a number of outstanding engineers and physicists, some of whom had been working on a nearly completed classified program in CSL. In addition, skilled electronics technicians and machinists soon joined the project.

In 1957 Nordsieck and Knoebel went to work on a gyro design incorporating a spherical rotor. Alpert kept in close touch with the project, but as the newly appointed director of CSL he had many other responsibilities. Following earlier conversations with Nordsieck about supporting a perfectly spherical rotor, Knoebel had built a simple model to demonstrate the principles and limitations of electrical levitation. The model showed that such levitation was possible if the vacuum was an extraordinarily good one and if the ball was feather light. Nordsieck was sensitive about the term "levitation" when the project started because, as he put it, "it sounds too much like magic." But no one ever suggested a less science-fiction sounding term, and the use of the word became commonplace.

During the early part of the project the researchers concentrated on rotor design. Experiments were conducted with two-inch-diameter solid aluminum balls obtained from bearing companies, but it soon became clear that even the aluminum balls were too heavy.

The experimenters began to look for materials lighter than aluminum with the correct electrical properties. The metal would have to be strong, light, and a good conductor of electricity. On the basis of available data Nordsieck and Knoebel concluded that titanium should be suitable, and had a rotor constructed from this difficult-to-work metal. Its electrical resistivity was too high: the standard reference sources had erred on this property of titanium. It was now obvious that the men could trust only their own findings and judgments about the little-known materials and techniques they were going to use. Working at or beyond the limits of knowledge in a number of fields, they could not rely on handbooks, previous projects, or other engineers' opinions. They began to consider each step carefully, assuming nothing to be correct until they had experimental verification of their own. In the long run this policy proved wise.

Next they tested a hollow aluminum ball. Although this type of rotor was light enough, they found that aluminum could not be machined to the tolerances required. The rotors had to be spherical to within a few millionths of an

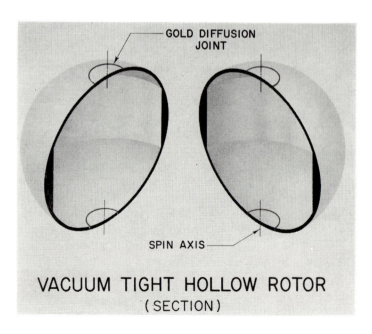

GOLD DIFFUSION JOINT

SPIN AXIS

VACUUM TIGHT HOLLOW ROTOR
(SECTION)

inch, and so carefully balanced that the weight of a finger-print would throw them off completely.

The material that finally proved successful for the rotors was beryllium. Because the dust produced during the machining of this unusual metal is poisonous to human beings, the parts machined had to be bathed in a dust-catching fluid. The balls were two inches in diameter, made as halves joined at the equator, and cost about $6,000 each to produce.

The Cadillac-priced rotors were fragile. Once one of the members of the group was carrying a ball when he stumbled over an electric cord: the ball, of course, did not bounce. On another occasion the power was cut accidentally during a levitation test, letting the fast-spinning rotor fall onto the electrodes—and it didn't bounce then, either.

The task of building the oxygen-free copper electrodes that would surround the ball and produce the electric fields to support it was not simple. The inner surfaces of these concave discs had to match the contour of the sphere closely. In the final design there were six electrodes, each about an inch in diameter, held in place by eight ceramic washers. When the electrodes and washers were fitted together, they formed a spherical chamber just a few thousandths of an inch larger than the beryllium ball.

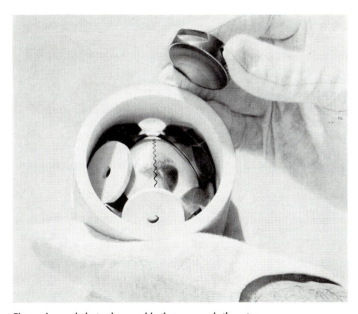

The washer and electrode assembly that surrounds the rotor

Now that these problems had been solved, a critical question remained: How could its users "read" the position of the ball? If it did work, how could they learn anything about the ball's direction of rotation without touching it? Nordsieck and Knoebel and their co-workers worked on this problem for months. Many schemes were advanced and discussed, one of which was to make portions of the rotor's surface radioactive so that its motion could be detected with a Geiger counter. The group ultimately decided, however, that the system would have to be optical to avoid disturbing the ball. They designed a system which beamed a light through special windows onto the rotor, illuminating

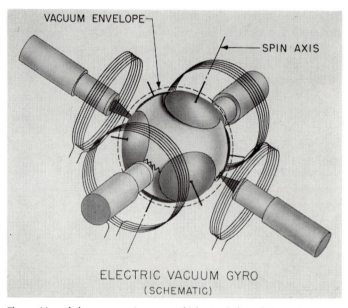

The position of the gyroscope's rotor could be read through four microscopes which were trained on a special zig-zag line on the surface of the ball.

it for four photo-microscopes which would watch it and feed their readings to a computer. But what would the instruments watch?

Finally Knoebel and Nordsieck decided to put a zig-zag line around the ball's equator. Nothing was commercially available that could hold the ball and ink a line around it, so they built a machine for the job. The inked line upset the delicate balance of the ball. Next the inking machine was converted to a miniature sand blaster that would only roughen the surface of the rotor. The technique worked.

The rotor's balance remained perfect, and the zig-zag line was permanent. Now only a few major problems remained: how to create and maintain a sufficiently high vacuum, how to make a housing for the rotor assembly, and how to shield out stray magnetic fields.

Alpert made the vacuum system work. The ultrahigh vacuum was necessary for two reasons: first, to work properly the ball had to be friction-free, even from contact with air molecules; and second, in a good vacuum about 100 times more weight could be levitated because the vacuum was a better electrical insulator than air. Thus higher voltages could be used to produce stronger supporting fields without causing sparks to jump from the electrodes to the ball.

The first vacuum system was crude. The entire gyro assembly had to be placed in a bell jar which was then evacuated of air. This arrangement made it difficult to operate the device as it would have to be operated for navigational uses. Studies of ways to build a demountable vacuum-tight housing were begun.

For months the creation of a suitable ceramic housing seemed an impossible task. To be mechanically stable the housing needed a high alumina content, which meant that its fabrication required much higher temperatures than most commercial kilns could produce. But the housing also had to contain four sapphire windows (for the photomicroscopes) and four molybdenum electrical feed-throughs (for the levitation electrodes). It had to be designed so that the rotor assembly could be inserted or removed, yet sealed tightly enough to contain the vacuum.

The job of building the housing fell to Nick Vassos, a technician experienced in building successful vacuum systems. Vassos had a reputation much like Knoebel's: he believed that any problem could be solved. At times during the construction of the housing he almost gave up this belief.

Vassos not only had to perform the difficult job of putting metals and ceramics together, but he also had to hold tolerances as close as 50 millionths of an inch. The heat required to fuse the sapphire windows to the housing would cause the housing to expand to the wrong size, and when the molybdenum pins were put in later, the second application of heat would cause the windows to loosen and fall out. "Who said any problem can be solved?" Vassos

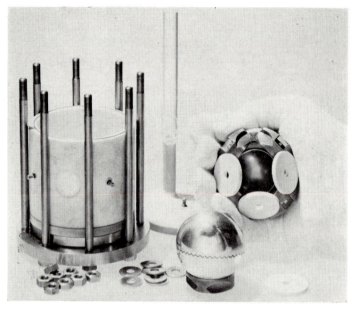

The ceramic housing and rotor, electrode, and washer assembly

asked other members of the team as the efforts to fabricate a housing dragged on.

Vassos and his colleagues finally managed to build a device that would push the windows and pins into place in the furnace and hold them while they were fused. Through the use of this jig they ultimately managed to build a perfect housing. Vassos was ecstatic. It was perfect, the only one in the world, and to him it was beautiful. After it was cool, he picked it up carefully and started upstairs to show it to Knoebel. Part way up he fell, and the housing was shattered. "I wish it had been my head," Vassos groaned.

Another housing was built, and it worked perfectly. The gyro was brought out of the bell jar and, under Alpert's guidance, the researchers set to work building a system to achieve the required vacuum in the housing. They adapted a special purpose pump which was mounted permanently on the housing to maintain the ultrahigh vacuum. They found that the rotor housing could be evacuated to one hundred billionth of atmospheric pressure, and assumed that they were over the last hurdle.

All that remained was to levitate and spin the rotor. Four electric coils to create spinning magnetic fields and acceler-

Gyro housing, complete with electric coils used to accelerate and stabilize the rotor

ate the ball were fastened to the outside of the housing. If the ball levitated, it would spin, and if it spun, it would work—or so the reasoning in the lab went. The rotor would be accelerated for only a few minutes; then the power would be turned off and it would "coast" on with nothing to slow it down.

In April, 1960, the gyro was completely assembled. Nordsieck, Knoebel, Alpert, and the others who had contributed were present. The switch was thrown, and after a moment Nordsieck said, "It's up and it's spinning." His exuberance was short-lived: there followed a pop like the bang of a cap pistol; the entire housing vibrated and then stood still. The gyro had failed.

When the assembly was torn down they found the rotor shattered. Their diagnosis was high-voltage vacuum breakdown—an electric spark had arced from an electrode to the spinning ball, upsetting its balance, causing it to hit the electrodes, destroying them and itself. Thousands of dollars and man-years of work were lost in the shattered gyro, but hardest to face was the fact that it could happen again with the next one. It was not a happy day in CSL.

Nordsieck, always sensitive to other people and their worries, was concerned about his co-workers' morale after the failure. He knew how much of themselves they had put into the gyro. The Lab's reorganization into the Coordi-

Arnold Nordsieck, the inventor of the electric vacuum gyro, displays the rotor, housing, and vacuum pump.

nated Science Laboratory the year before had marked the achievement of one of the project's goals, the departure from purely classified research. But this success would be little solace if the gyro itself failed. After much discussion and study, all of them agreed that theoretically the idea should still work—and they could come to only one conclusion about the failure: they decided they needed cleaner surfaces and a better vacuum.

"Clean surfaces" to these men had a different meaning

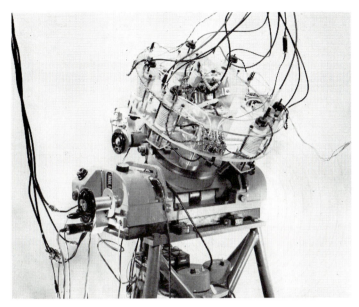

This gyro test stand used electric motors to maintain the orientation of the rotor with its optical sensors.

than it has for housewives. It meant cleanness on the atomic scale. The researchers had to be sure that there were so few contaminants on the surfaces of the ball and the electrodes that high-voltage sparks would not jump across as electrical shorts. The need for a better vacuum was in reality a need for better insulation between the electrodes and the rotor: the better the vacuum, the fewer the molecules of contaminating vapors which could carry a spark.

A few weeks later, in June of 1960, the team members prepared for another test. They had achieved a vacuum of a millionth of a millionth of atmospheric pressure. "It's going to work this time," Nordsieck said as the ball was suspended and then brought up to speed. After a few minutes of acceleration, the power to the induction coils was turned off. The ball continued spinning silently at 12,000 rpm. Effectively isolated from the rest of the universe, it should go on spinning for years.

The only thing that remained was to verify the gyro's accuracy. It was aimed at the North Star and tested from June, 1960, through December, 1963. It was more accurate than the researchers had dared to hope. The "star in a bottle," as the Navy would call it, had been born.

THE WORLD OF SUPERCOLD

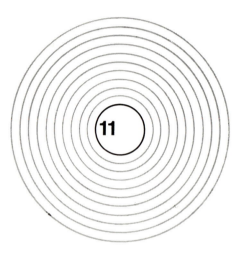

"Extraordinarily gifted and second to none," said the editors of *Fortune* of John Bardeen. There was ample evidence for their statement. Bardeen and two of his colleagues at Bell Telephone Laboratories had invented the transistor, the tiny device that revolutionized the electronics industry. They had won a Nobel prize and international renown for explaining the behavior of electrons on the surfaces of solids. But the prize, the fame, even the transistor itself were far less important to Bardeen than the knowledge he and his co-workers had gathered in developing the transistor. The three men were physicists.

The physicist must often observe, and sometimes create, extreme environments to gain an understanding of something about the universe. He observes the characteristics of the astronomical bodies in the heavens as well as the submicroscopic objects of the atomic world. He experiments with pressures ranging from several hundred thousand atmospheres to those too low to support a column of mercury one atom high. He works with temperatures so high that they disintegrate all the atoms of a gas into ions, and temperatures low enough to approach the ultimate in cold.

The physicist, who thinks of temperature as a measure of the "internal energy" of materials—the constant motion of the molecules—uses the Kelvin scale to measure temperatures. The lowest point on this scale is absolute zero, which is the lowest temperature in the universe. Zero (0°K) equals −459.67° Fahrenheit.

The world of low temperatures is one of the most exciting in all of physics. Near 0°K, rubber becomes extremely brittle; lead becomes springy and resilient; and copper gets stronger. With the exception of helium, all gases become solids at very low temperatures. Helium becomes a liquid at 4.2°K and remains such to absolute zero. Below 2.186°K it

Liquid helium is transferred from a storage vessel into an apparatus for measuring the magnetic properties of superconductors.

becomes a superfluid, displaying an ability to flow without friction or viscosity through holes too small to pass any gas or ordinary liquid. Superfluid helium seems to defy gravity: if a test tube is partially immersed in it, the superfluid will spontaneously creep up the walls of the tube and over the lip until the levels inside and out are the same. When the test tube is lifted from the superfluid, the liquid will creep over the lip of the tube until it is emptied.

An equally strange phenomenon of the world of ultralow temperatures is superconductivity. In 1911 Kammerlingh Onnes, a Dutch physicist, found that all resistance to the flow of electricity disappeared from mercury when it was cooled to $4.15°$K. In later years it was discovered that many other metallic elements exhibited superconductivity, each at its own particular temperature, but all at close to $0°$K. Oddly enough, the best electrical conductors, copper and silver, did not prove to be superconductive; in fact gold, an excellent conductor, could be used as insulation for superconducting wire. But experiments showed that currents induced in a closed ring of superconducting wire would flow for years without apparent diminution in strength.

The phenomenon of superconductivity suggested an obvious practical application. Before 1915 attempts were made to use superconducting wires to carry strong currents without resistive losses. The results were unsatisfactory because the magnetic field associated with an electric current converted the superconducting wire back to its normal resistive state, even though the temperature was still low enough for superconductivity. The few known superconductors returned to normal in relatively low magnetic fields, so interest in practical applications languished.

While Onnes was working with superconductivity, Lord Ernest Rutherford was performing his famous experiments which led to the "discovery" of the atomic nucleus. By 1950 nuclear physics had produced a vast technology based upon this knowledge, but superconductivity was still a baffling scientific curiosity. The intervening 40 years had been occupied largely with patient experimental attempts to catalog all the pertinent properties of superconductors in the hope that some theorist would be able to put the pieces together. Such great men as Niels Bohr, Werner Heisenberg, Wolfgang Pauli, and Fritz London had worked on the problem with only limited success.

In 1951 John Bardeen came to Illinois to work with Professor Frederick Seitz and the other members of the solid state physics group. He spent much of his time trying to develop a theory that would explain superconductivity, a subject which had interested him since the 1930's. In 1950 he had written a theory which, like the several others already advanced, had proved unsatisfactory. But these theories did indicate the direction in which advances might be expected.

Two other men who had come to Illinois worked with Bardeen on the problem: Leon Cooper and J. Robert Schrieffer. Cooper was a brilliant young expert in the theories of the nucleus and of elementary particles, but he had never worked in solid state physics. Arriving in the fall of 1955, he shared an office with Bardeen. He brought some important concepts from high energy physics to bear on the problem of superconductivity.

Schrieffer had come to Illinois in 1953 from MIT, where he had acquired a reputation as an outstanding student. At Illinois he worked toward his Ph.D. under Bardeen's direction, and by the summer of 1956 he was ready to select a topic for his doctoral thesis.

The three men made an interesting group because of their obvious contrasts. Bardeen was a full professor and a physicist with an international reputation. Cooper was a research associate working in a field for which he had not been trained. Schrieffer was a graduate student trying to finish his education. The two younger men were lively, jovial, and talkative, while Bardeen was shy and retiring.

In the fall of 1955 the three physicists began discussing the mystery of superconductivity. Bardeen had just completed a long review article which summarized the state of knowledge and the outstanding unsolved questions in the field. It was a complex and baffling phenomenon, and the men spent months examining possible explanations for its apparently contradictory characteristics. They explored many attractive hypotheses, to find that all failed in one way or another. Finally the trio made a long intuitive leap to the basis for a new superconductivity theory. It was a daring piece of educated guesswork.

The theory, known as the Bardeen, Cooper, Schrieffer microscopic theory of superconductivity, or more simply as the BCS theory, was not simple. It depended heavily upon the principles of quantum mechanics, postulating that superconductivity is a condensation phenomenon, somewhat analogous to a gas condensing into a liquid. The three men speculated that some metals lose their electrical resistivity at extremely low temperatures because the electron "gas" which permeates their atomic lattice condenses into a superfluid or superliquid. In this liquid state the electrons are bound together into a single quantum system or huge "molecule" which extends throughout the entire sample. The electrons flow as a group through the metal without resistance, much like the friction-free flow of the superfluid helium.

Physicists found that the theory, together with its subsequent developments, agreed with a wide variety of known phenomena. While the theory was still being developed, one facet was verified experimentally at Illinois in a research project begun before the theory was proposed.

Many physicists felt that if Bardeen had not won the Nobel prize for the invention of the transistor, he would certainly have won it for the theory of superconductivity. He himself felt that the theory was the more significant piece of work. He was awarded the Fritz London prize for it in 1962, and a National Medal of Science in 1966.

Research activity on superconductivity and related fields increased tremendously after the theory was published. Subsequent work suggested that some concepts of the BCS theory play nearly as basic a role in theories of nuclear structure as they do in the explanation of superconductivity. A number of physicists began work on theories of elementary particles based on analogies with the BCS theory.

The better understanding of superconductivity brought about by the BCS theory has also helped to stimulate applications of the phenomenon. Some of the new superconducting devices being built are computer components, sensitive measuring instruments, high-precision gyroscopes, components that will greatly improve the power of electron microscopes, and small but extremely powerful superconducting magnets. Indeed, superconducting magnets weighing ten pounds have replaced conventional electromagnets weighing 750 pounds. One such magnet still in use requires 1,700,000 watts of power and 1,000 gallons of water per minute to remove the heat generated in the copper windings. A superconducting magnet with the same field strength, which requires no water for cooling, uses a six-volt battery for power (300 watts) and a 10,000 watt refrigerator to maintain the supercold environment. One of the keys to making such magnets was the discovery of materials that would remain superconductive under very high magnetic fields. The BCS theory has helped physicists understand the properties of such materials.

A current research program at Illinois illustrates another use for superconductivity. A conventional linear accelerator hurls particles, either electrons or protons, in one-

The small superconducting magnet in the man's hand is three times more powerful than the conventional electromagnet to the right.

millionth-of-a-second bursts through tubular metal waveguides. The walls of the waveguides are intended simply to guide the energy, but they turn much of it into heat because of their electrical resistance. Because the walls heat so quickly, the accelerator must be stopped frequently to cool. If these waveguides are made of superconducting material, however, power can be applied continuously—and the accelerator will emit electrons in a continuous stream.

These are some of the results of "understanding," and, as Bardeen points out, applied superconductivity is still a brand-new technology. The real results, some of the best of which may show up in the space program, are still to come. The low temperatures required for superconducting devices would be easier to achieve and maintain in space or on the moon.

One possible future application of great interest to scientists and engineers is the creation of "magnetic bottles" for containing nuclear fusion energy. Controlled nuclear fusion, which, like the sun, would produce nearly limitless energy from hydrogen, is a dream that predates the exploding of the first H-bomb. The reaction would generate temperatures of about 100 million degrees centigrade. No known material could possibly hold the inferno of a fusion reac-

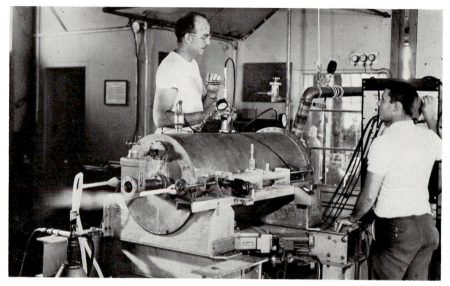

This superconducting linear accelerator is being developed at Illinois. Instrument panels at right are the cooling and radio-frequency controls.

tion, but a magnetic field of sufficient strength could theoretically do so.

If ordinary electromagnets were used to create such a field, the power required would be incredibly large, possibly exceeding the output of the reaction itself. Many researchers feel that superconducting magnets may be the answer to creating such invisible "magnetic bottles." When this becomes a reality, scientists and engineers will be using ultralow temperatures to contain ultrahigh temperatures. And they will have gained this ability because three physicists, uninterested in such applications, brought a bit of understanding in out of the cold.

A COMPUTER
IN THE CLASSROOM

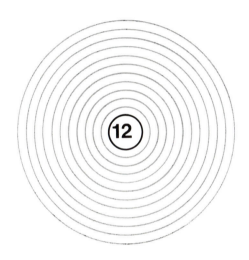

"Education," wrote Sidney L. Pressey, a noted educational psychologist, "is the one major activity in this country which is still in the crude handicraft stage." It was 1932. Pressey proposed to bring education into the machine age with a teaching machine—a simple desk-top apparatus designed to administer and score tests.

In 1959 a physicist repeated Pressey's challenge, and answered it with a question: "There hasn't been a great invention in the field of education since the book. Why couldn't computers be applied to education?"

The physicist was Chalmers Sherwin, Associate Director of the University of Illinois Control Systems Laboratory. The remedy he envisioned for the situation was the same one Pressey had prescribed almost three decades earlier—the teaching machine. In the very phrasing of his statement, Sherwin summed up the impact of the Pressey machine and its successors. They had impressed, amused, or offended educational theorists, but had scarcely affected the American classroom.

Pictured above is one of several simple teaching machines developed in the 1920's by Sidney L. Pressey of The Ohio State University. The machine rewarded students with candies in return for correct answers to test questions.

The difference in Sherwin's suggestion was a vital one— the computer. Twenty-seven years of technological progress had brought into existence a device Pressey could scarcely have imagined—one seldom fully appreciated even by Sherwin's contemporaries. So esoteric were the attributes of the computer, in fact, that a University committee formed in response to Sherwin's question was hobbled by the variety of its members' views of what could and should be done. Daniel Alpert, Director of the Control Systems Laboratory, chaired the committee, which was composed of educators, psychologists, mathematicians, and engineers. The men could not compromise on either a pilot course or a system with which to present it. A report by one committee member mentioned an important element of the dilemma:

The most critical personnel problem remains to be discussed: that of overall direction of the project. This is a truly interdisciplinary project . . . in the disciplines of education, psychology, and engineering. . . . Without an appreciation of all the components in the program on the part of the leader, the project will be crippled if not doomed.

Alpert was troubled by this conclusion. The possibilities of computers in education looked tremendously attractive. He described his feelings in a report he began to write to

Dean William L. Everitt. The chief obstacle, he noted, seemed to be the impossibility of finding a project director who was both an educator and a computer expert.

The report lay unsigned on Alpert's desk when he left that evening. The next day he flew to a conference in Washington, with the unsatisfying result of the committee's search still on his mind. During the return flight, he recalls, it occurred to him that "We might have overlooked something. Part of our problem had been that only the educators and psychologists knew enough about most kinds of teaching to know what to aim for. But we at CSL were as interested and competent as anyone in one field of education—teaching computer programming."

Dean Everitt never saw the initial report. Instead, a few days later, he read a prognosis of a very different sort:

. . . the advent of the high-speed computer makes possible a new approach to education. . . . The first research objective will be toward the design of *an automatic "teaching machine" to teach students at various levels how to use a high-speed computer.* This particular objective is especially suited to the talent and motivation of the people who would have to design such a machine and represents a unique educational need in the coming decade. . . .

So Alpert, in effect, ignored his committee's disunity. Instead he started looking for a man with a special set of qualifications: "What we wanted was an inventor. From what I'd seen in the past of invention, of creativity, I knew the project would have to go to someone with both the ability to design a very different kind of machine and the motivation to try it."

That man, he decided, was Donald Bitzer. Bitzer was young—only twenty-six—and had earned his Ph.D. in electrical engineering only six months before. A project like this would be a big responsibility, if it were possible at all. (Bitzer later concluded, "Perhaps the main reason I got the chance was that most of the people with more experience didn't think the project had a prayer.") But Bitzer's background was impressive: he had spent his last four years in CSL and had made valuable contributions to radar studies and other projects involving computers. He had, in addition, an infectious kind of personal dynamism. For relaxation he might run 15 miles cross-country, and he usually worked "on the run" as well. His enthusiasm was known to spring forth sometimes in the form of outrageously optimistic timetables and predictions, but at times he seemed able to push back the edge of the impossible. Coincidentally, Bitzer was an outspoken and creative critic of many aspects of conventional education—especially engineering education. To Alpert he looked like the perfect man for the teaching machine project.

Some of the educators and psychologists close to the project, however, were skeptical. Perhaps influenced by professional pride, they disagreed with Alpert's idea that the subject of computer programming was such new and foreign educational territory that engineers were as competent to explore it as anyone. Bitzer himself may have alarmed some observers. Aggressive and blunt, he might have looked like an added risk for an already uncertain project.

But Bitzer was far from uncertain about the project. Together with another Laboratory computer expert, mathematician Peter Braunfeld, he set out to design a system that would enable a computer to teach its potential users how to use it. In designing the circuitry for the teaching system he faced a problem at the start that he would meet again and again: how to transform the "art" of teaching into a science.

Two rival philosophies of automatic teaching had been developed by educational psychologists. One, developed by B. F. Skinner at Harvard in the early fifties, presented material to the student in elementary bits—bits cut so fine, in effect, that any student could digest them. The other system, credited chiefly to Norman A. Crowder of the Air Force Personnel Training and Research Center, presented lesson material in larger packages. These were interrelated so that a student who readily grasped the material could leapfrog through a minimum number of lessons, while a slower classmate would find himself directed both forward and backward through the total sequence of lessons until he understood the material thoroughly. Despite its greater complexity, Bitzer and Braunfeld chose the latter technique, "branched programming," because they felt it took better advantage of the computer's abilities. They sought, as had other builders of teaching machines, to blend into their system two important educational ingredients: rapid judgment of the student's grasp of ideas; and "feedback," the information about a student's reaction which the instructor must have to assess and improve his teaching.

The two men checked to see what others had done with computers in education. They found little. Experts in education were still primarily pursuing the course set by Pressey, with simple mechanical machines sometimes augmented by film projectors and sound equipment. Many of them were interested in teaching machines, but they seldom had the skills necessary to build complex, computer-based systems. The Systems Development Corporation, IBM, and others had experimented with computers in education, but generally had used a minimum of special equipment.

"It looked as though even the people with computers weren't using them very much," recalls Bitzer. "In some cases a person could have replaced the computer without much effort. So Braunfeld and I decided we were on our own. We wanted to build a sophisticated general purpose teaching system that would really give the computer a workout. We knew that the results—if it worked—might be pretty impressive."

They decided to employ the University's ILLIAC I computer as the brains of the electronic outfit. By using a large, general purpose computer they hoped to be able to test advanced teaching techniques and study a wide variety of teaching methods without making extensive changes in their original equipment.

Braunfeld developed the basic teaching logic (the pattern of computer operations required) for the system. One part of his experience proved particularly worthwhile here: Braunfeld had been one of the chief programmers on the secret "Cornfield" radar tracking system developed by the Control Systems Laboratory during the Korean War. This system had contributed valuable knowledge about using a computer for making decisions automatically—as they would have to be made in a teaching program.

In seven days the two men designed the circuitry and logic for the system, and settled on a plan of organization:

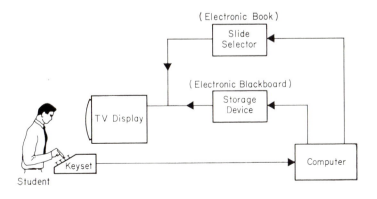

Shortly after the project began, the system was christened PLATO for "Programmed Logic for Automatic Teaching Operations." According to Bitzer the title met some ridicule: "People claimed that it took us two weeks to find a word starting with 'O' for the end of the acronym."

The summer passed in a frenzy of building and testing because the researchers had decided to show a sample of their work at a meeting of the CSL's sponsored in three months. The project was operating with a small staff and a low budget, so many components were borrowed, made from leftovers, or "stolen" from elsewhere. At one point the petty cash fund for the project was tapped for $20 to buy two secondhand television sets which were patched sufficiently to make them work for the demonstration. Finally, two hours before the meeting began, everything worked. "It was quite a gamble," says Bitzer. "Everything about the system was untried, and it was all patched together. But it ran without a hitch all through the conference."

The demonstration was a hit. It showed how ILLIAC I might teach a student to program ILLIAC I. The pupil sat at a telephone-booth-like station facing a television screen, and communicated with the computer through a key set like that of a typewriter with special keys.

Key set with which the PLATO student communicates with the computer.

The closest the project came to disaster was five months later, at the first demonstration of the use of a remote student station, 20 miles from the campus. On the morning of the demonstration Bitzer discovered that a storm had felled the telephone line the equipment was to use. Although the line was intact, its electrical characteristics as it lay on the ground differed from those the teaching equipment was designed for. Without much hope Bitzer made the few adjustments of which the hastily built equipment was capable—and soon had it operating.

With growing support from University officials, the work continued. Within a year PLATO I became PLATO II with the addition of another teaching station and changes in the teaching logic which allowed subjects other than computer programming to be taught. Their initial success with the subject of computer programming had encouraged the group to expand PLATO's applications. Experts in other fields were consulted for the expansion. The main purpose of the change was to test the feasibility of using the computer to teach students in groups rather than singly. The problems encountered in coping with two students differed only in degree from those of teaching hundreds or perhaps thousands of pupils simultaneously.

In a PLATO classroom sudents seated in individual booths read the lessons from a television screen, and type their responses on small key sets.

The problem of numbers was successfully met, and PLATO II was expanded to become PLATO III, a truly polydextrous teacher with 20 student stations and a variety of teaching techniques. PLATO's previous computer, the ILLIAC I, was replaced with a commercially built CDC 1604, which was much faster and had a larger memory. Bitzer's calculations indicated that the new PLATO might teach as many as a thousand students eight different lessons simultaneously, without neglecting anyone.

The key to its fluency was that PLATO was designed to converse with its students sequentially: imagine a harried executive with a telephone in either hand, his head flipping back and forth in a blur, carrying on two conversations like "By/Certainly,/Thursday,/dear,/Grimsbee,/I'll/sell/stop/those/at/six/the/hundred/cleaner's/shares/on/of/my/Gibraltar/way/Paperweight/home." Imagine him now with a thousand telephones, answering each so quickly that no one imagines that his mind is elsewhere, and the picture might fit PLATO at work.

Watching PLATO is the best way to understand how the system operates. A seventh-grader studying a PLATO geometry lesson sits at a small booth. In front of him at eye level is a television screen, and on the shelf is the electric key set. With the keys the student turns pages, writes in answers, and can ask for help. He switches the machine on, and page one appears on the screen:

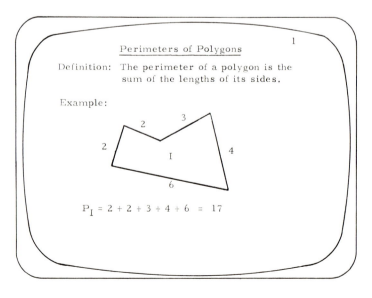

Perimeters of Polygons

Definition: The perimeter of a polygon is the sum of the lengths of its sides.

Example:

$P_I = 2 + 2 + 3 + 4 + 6 = 17$

The youngster reads the slide, presses his "continue" key, and sees page 2:

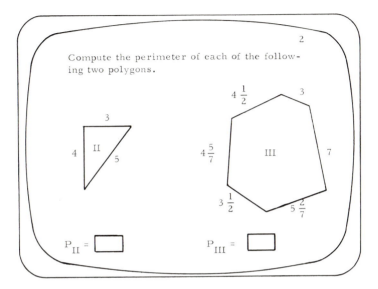

As the student types "12," the numbers appear in the first box. To see whether his answer is correct he presses the key marked "judge," and the verdict "OK" appears behind his answer:

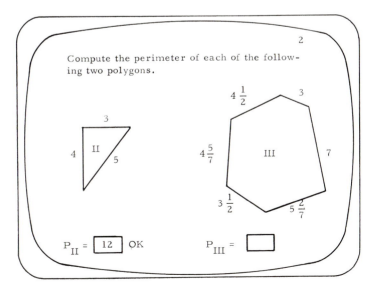

Perhaps overconfident with his first success, he hurries through the second part, answers "27," and again presses the "judge" key:

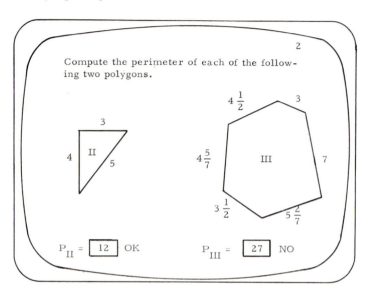

Noting his mistake, the student presses a key marked "erase," types in "28," and again presses "judge."

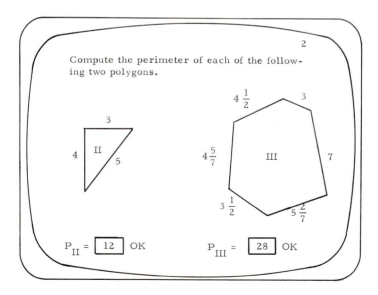

If his second attempt were also incorrect, the student could continue erasing and trying again for as long as his persistence lasts. Or he could press the key marked "reverse" and return to page 1 for review. But only when page 2 has been correctly answered can he turn to page 3. He presses the "continue" key and sees a new slide:

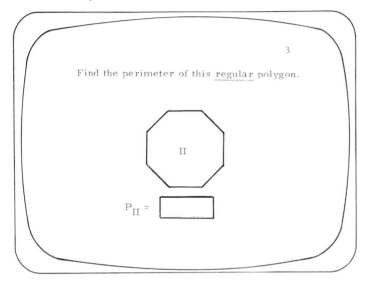

Here he is stymied, however. So he presses the key marked "help" and sees this special slide:

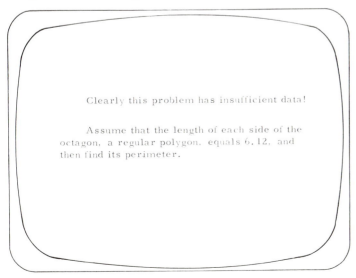

With the additional information he sees his way to the answer, and thus enlightened presses a key marked "aha" to return to the problem. With page 3 again before him, he types "48.96," presses his "judge" key, and is relieved to see the result:

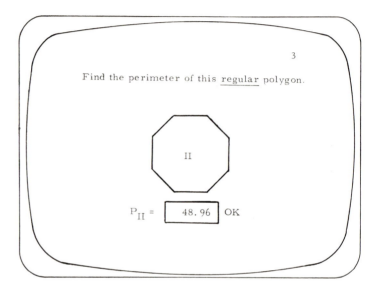

There are other tricks PLATO's human programmer can use to teach the student. If an answer is simply misspelled, for instance, the "judge" operation will return a decision of "SP" and the word must be corrected. PLATO's "help" slides may be specially matched to the kinds of errors commonly made and may explain the subject in more detail, present supplementary questions or problems, or provide clues toward answering the original question. But if even the "help" sequences fail to get the student past his difficulty, he can electronically look in the back of the book by pushing his "answer" button. The correct answer will appear in its proper place on the page.

However, the student isn't fooling anyone by not supplying his own answer. PLATO keeps a record for each student of every request for help, every wrong answer, and even how much time was spent on each page. This record also provides information about the lessons themselves. Text pages which are exceptionally easy or difficult can be spotted immediately; and, more important, criticisms about the course as a whole can be made from either the original

PLATO data or from the computer's summaries of those data.

The emphasis Bitzer and Braunfeld placed on using the computer unsparingly has paid dividends. For example, a given slide can be selected in less than a millionth of a second. This speed would be impossible with any sort of mechanical selector, so PLATO's inventors developed an entirely electronic system to do the job. A beam of light is electronically aimed at a selected slide, and a sensing tube relays the picture to the student's television screen. The electronic blackboard plots diagrams, symbols, and words point-by-point on the television screen at either the computer's or student's command. With this arrangement unpredicted information can be shown, such as answers composed by the student himself, or graphs whose characteristics the student specifies. A student's answer to a PLATO question can be checked not only by comparing it to a given correct answer (of which, to some problems, there may be infinitely many), but also by using it in calculations to test its own validity. And the student himself can use the computer for calculations required to solve a problem.

PLATO can change the pace of its teaching to fit the student's ability: if he grasps key material readily, PLATO may present him with either the regular or an accelerated text. If his answers and requests for help indicate trouble, PLATO may present the text lessons in more easily digestible bits without requiring him to request the regular "help" sequence. If he finds something about the lesson or its presentation particularly delightful or irritating, the student can electronically turn to a "comment" page and record his opinion there. Or he can talk with his (human) instructor.

PLATO can switch from this "tutorial" method of teaching to others entirely different. For example, an "Inquiry Logic" has been prepared for the system which lets it imitate a laboratory, a sick patient to be tended, or any other situation which forces the student to seek information on his own. The inquiry logic provides the student with a way of phrasing his questions so that the computer can understand them. In essence he is provided with a treelike system of choices: after he makes his initial choice of what information he desires, he is presented with a second choice which specifies this information still further, then a third, a fourth, and so on, until his question has been asked as precisely as he cares to ask it.

An advanced problem-solving logic for the computer lets the student formulate his own problems and conjectures, and work them out with the same supervision as if they had been created by the author of the text lesson. It is also possible to interconnect PLATO stations and use them in ways that originally were not foreseen. Intriguing "diplomacy games" and "war games" can be played by students at two or more stations who act and react to each other's decisions and to the unforeseeable developments of fate, whose role is played by PLATO.

Two questions commonly arise about the author of a PLATO course: Is he a teacher, or simply a technician? Must he be a computer expert? To the first question—he is certainly a teacher, and in fact must be an especially talented one, since the lessons he prepares will be followed more closely (and possibly by more students) than conventional presentations.

The second question can be answered in several ways. First, the PLATO author need not be familiar with computers at all. PLATO's builders have developed an "author mode" with which the author, seated at a regular student station, can describe his text to the computer in a relatively simple way and let the machine adapt his lessons to fit the PLATO system. Or the teacher may enter more sophisticated teaching logics by using conventional computer programming techniques.

But what about the teacher? Is PLATO an omen that automation will displace him? Pressey wrote in 1926 that "It would seem highly desirable to lift from the teacher's shoulders as much as possible of this burden and make [the teacher] freer for those inspirational and thought-stimulating activities which are, presumably, [his] real function. . . ." Bitzer agrees, adding, "PLATO would let teachers be sympathetic advisers—not just clerks."

How does PLATO rate as a teacher? If it were flawless, of course, its pupils would not welcome as they do the occasional conferences with a human instructor. An obvious observation can be made that PLATO simply hasn't a human face or voice. This facelessness, of course, also frees PLATO from human mannerisms, preferences, and emotions.

Because the system lets each student work at his own pace, the brighter student who completes his required work early may study optional material in that course or in another subject. Each student could spend all his time learning new material, neither impeded nor hurried past half-learned ideas.

Experimental teaching programs tried with PLATO demonstrate the versatility of the system. Mathematics courses ranging in difficulty from a second-grade lesson with a zoo theme to college-senior-level lessons introducing Maxwell's equations have been used; three courses related to computers and their use have grown out of the original PLATO idea; and other lessons have taught such varied subjects as use of the library, recognition of letters (for two- and three-year-olds), methods of scientific inquiry based on real and synthetic laboratory experiments, and Braille translation. For the first time, University credit courses taught wholly or in part by machine have been offered in electrical engineering, commerce, and library science. The courses, offered to undergraduates, have grown rapidly in popularity.

Another kind of study is interesting for the science-fiction possibilities it brings to mind: students were fitted with instruments which measured their heart rates as they studied PLATO lessons, and significant changes were noted at those moments when they acquired insights into new concepts. Perhaps one day, if these results could be expanded, a student taught by machine might not have to make any conscious comments: his physiological reaction might provide his automatic instructor with all the guidance it needs. Exams could be a thing of the past.

Not everyone's praise for PLATO's past is unreserved. Among educators, for example, there is occasional criticism of the way PLATO has been used and of the ideas behind some of its features. One complaint is that, like almost every other system of mass instruction, PLATO ignores the student's particular interests and abilities. Some feel that the whole aim of PLATO's builders has been at the wrong target, that instead of intending it for the use of masses of regular students they should first use it to help the smaller group of students who have difficulty learning by conventional means. The present expense of PLATO instruction is a strong argument in support of this contention (a computer suitable for PLATO use costs hundreds of thousands of dollars, and each student station requires nearly $3,000's worth of components). In addition, PLATO's ability to change teaching personalities to suit the occasion would seem particularly appropriate for slow learners.

Several important changes will be incorporated into PLATO IV, which is under construction. The new system will have its own computer, motion-picture displays, and a voice as well. The Control Data Corporation has lent a computer especially for the project. A special system of recorded messages will eventually let PLATO give verbal directions, make judgments, and answer questions.

One of the most consistent results of learning studies made with PLATO is that the computer's students do *not* learn more thoroughly than those taught the same lessons by human instructors—but they usually cover their subjects in about half the time. Thus PLATO and others of its breed may make their first important appearance not in schools, but rather in industries and in the armed forces. Industry is interested because it wants to be able to take employees from widely different backgrounds and train them to a relatively standard degree of competence in a particular job. The armed services' task is similar, but since their period of contact with most individuals is relatively short, less time lost in training means a valuable increase in the percentage of time that their personnel spend in useful jobs.

According to Bitzer, however, "Except for a few school experiments, automatic teaching systems will probably find their first acceptance in the home. For the price of a color television set a family could install a student station and tune in lessons in all kinds of subjects. Besides lessons for school children, they might have college courses, adult education courses, or courses designed to upgrade professional skills. There might be other services such as news and weather reports. I think interested individuals will bring the computer into education long before the public provides the tax money to put the new system into public schools." The idea may not be as far-fetched as it sounds. Expense, the biggest obstacle to such a change, is being overcome as computers become simpler, smaller, cheaper, and more reliable.

Bitzer recognized that a natural obstacle to this use would be the high cost of special closed-circuit television sets to allow communication with the central computer. He and his colleagues have invented a display tube to replace the conventional cathode-ray tube—a development that may make more compact, less expensive TV sets available in the near future. This device, no thicker than a piece of plate glass, not only has the ability to produce images, but can also retain them. In the language of electronics, it has a "memory." The applications of this invention could range from "hang-on-the-wall" television sets to important new display elements for computers.

Others foresee broader areas of PLATO's impact on education: first, in the University itself; second, in the increasingly popular junior colleges, where PLATO stations might enable communities of schools to share special skills and facilities; and last, in high schools, which might be linked to universities via PLATO stations.

But the future of PLATO cannot be foretold. Risk is an inseparable part of any activity which, like research, must stay ahead of the times. Daniel Alpert, who catalyzed the reaction which resulted in PLATO, sees the project's significance as great: "When the printing press was invented, it was produced to print Bibles. No one could imagine that one day there would be newspapers, novels, or comic books. I think that PLATO is the same kind of idea—that we simply can't foresee its uses because of our limited experience."

The first regular college courses taught by a computer are being offered to U of I students with the PLATO system.

These grand expectations for the project may materialize. The University Board of Trustees has approved a plan to expand PLATO research into a University-wide Computer-based Education Research Laboratory. The new facility will bring PLATO out of the science laboratory and into broader contact with educators, psychologists, and others whose access to the system has been limited during its early development. The new facility will be established as a unit of the Graduate College, now headed by Alpert. Bitzer, the creative engineer behind PLATO, will remain in charge of the system's technical aspects.

Thus PLATO has attained the status of an operational system. The educators have provided perhaps the surest testament to the device's success: they are interested in using it. But it remains an experiment still—perhaps now an even grander experiment. Mac E. Van Valkenberg, long a lab-mate of the project in CSL, and now Chairman of the Department of Electrical Engineering at Princeton, has said of the system, "Any predictions made for PLATO are speculation. It may be forgotten, or it may be the development of the century."

AUTHORS' NOTE

Every effort was made to accurately report dates, times, places, and other factual details in this book. We did use information based upon the memories of faculty members, alumni, and relatives of some of the characters in these stories, and conversations and situations from the past were recreated with the hope of portraying the people or incidents as accurately as possible. Quotes from letters, reports, and other publications are exact and can be documented.